Homework Helpers

Eureka Math
Grade 4

Special thanks go to the Gordan A. Cain Center and to the Department of Mathematics at Louisiana State University for their support in the development of *Eureka Math*.

Homework Helpers

Grade 4
Module 1

G4-M1-Lesson 1

1. Label the place value charts. Fill in the blanks to make the following equations true. Draw disks in the place value chart to show how you got your answer, using arrows to show any regrouping.

10×3 ones = ___30___ ones = ___3 tens___

thousands	hundreds	tens	ones

10 × 3 ones is represented by drawing 3 disks in the ones column and then drawing 9 more ones for each disk. 10 × 3 ones is 30 ones.

thousands	hundreds	tens	ones

I draw an arrow to the tens column to show I am regrouping 10 ones as 1 ten. 30 ones is the same as 3 tens.

2. Complete the following statements using your knowledge of place value. Then, use pictures, numbers, or words to explain how you got your answer.

   __60__ hundreds is the same as 6 thousands.

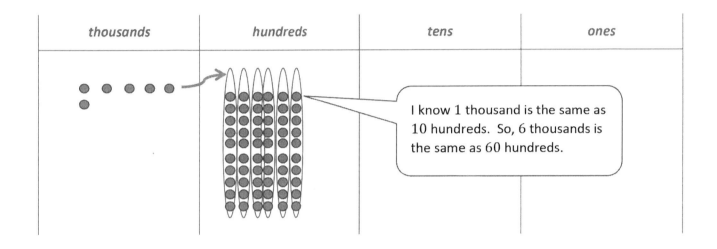

thousands	hundreds	tens	ones

I know 1 thousand is the same as 10 hundreds. So, 6 thousands is the same as 60 hundreds.

3. Gabby has 50 books in her room. Her mom has 10 times as many books in her office. How many books does Gabby's mom have? Use numbers or words to explain how you got your answer.

   5 tens × 10 = 50 tens

   Gabby's mom has 500 books in her office.

   50 tens is the same as 5 hundreds. I can write my answer in standard form within a sentence to explain my answer.

Lesson 1:   Interpret a multiplication equation as a comparison.

EUREKA MATH

G4-M1-Lesson 2

1. Label and represent the product or quotient by drawing disks on the place value chart.

    a.   10 × 3 thousands =   **30**   thousands =   *3 ten thousands*

millions	hundred thousands	ten thousands	thousands	hundreds	tens	ones

Just as in Lesson 1, I group each ten with a circle and draw an arrow to show I am regrouping 30 thousands as 3 ten thousands.

    b.   2 thousands ÷ 10 =   __20__   hundreds ÷ 10 =   __2 hundreds__

millions	hundred thousands	ten thousands	thousands	hundreds	tens	ones

I can't divide 2 thousands disks into equal groups of 10. So, I rename 2 thousands as 20 hundreds. Now, I can divide 20 hundreds into equal groups of 10.

EUREKA MATH   **Lesson 2:**   Recognize a digit represents 10 times the value of what it represents in tl place to its right.   **3**

©2015 Great Minds. eureka-math.org
G4-M1-HWH-1.3.0-07.2015

2. Solve for the expression by writing the solution in unit form and in standard form.

Expression	Unit Form	Standard Form
(3 tens 2 ones) × 10	30 *tens* 20 *ones*	320

I multiply each unit, the tens and the ones, by 10.

3. Solve.

   840 matches are in 1 box. 10 times as many matches are in a package. How many matches in a package?

   84 *tens* × 10 *is* 840 *tens or* 84 *hundreds.*

   $840 × 10 = 8,400$

   8,400 *matches are in a package.*

   I can use unit form to make the multiplication easier and to verify my answer in standard form.

Lesson 2:   Recognize a digit represents 10 times the value of what it represents in tl
                                  place to its right.

©2015 Great Minds. eureka-math.org
G4-M1-HWH-1.3.0-07.2015

G4-M1-Lesson 3

1. Rewrite the following number, including commas where appropriate:

   30030033003   __30,030,033,003__

   > I use a comma after every 3 digits from the right to indicate the periods, or grouping of units—ones, thousands, millions, and billions.

2. Solve each expression. Record your answer in standard form.

   > I can add 5 tens + 9 tens = 14 tens.

Expression	Standard Form
5 tens + 9 tens	140

   > 14 tens is the same as 10 tens and 4 tens. I can bundle 10 tens to make 1 hundred. 14 tens is the same as 140.

3. Represent each addend with place value disks in the place value chart. Show the composition of larger units from 10 smaller units. Write the sum in standard form.

   3 thousands + 14 hundreds = __4,400__

millions	hundred thousands	ten thousands	thousands	hundreds	tens	ones
			••• ●	⬭(●●●●● ●●●●● ●●●●)		

   > After drawing 3 thousands and 14 hundreds disks, I notice that 10 hundreds can be bundled as 1 thousand. Now, my picture shows 4 thousands 4 hundreds, or 4,400.

EUREKA MATH

Lesson 3: Name numbers within 1 million by building understanding of the place value chart and placement of commas for naming base thousand units.

©2015 Great Minds. eureka-math.org
G4-M1-HWH-1.3.0-07.2015

5

4. Use digits or disks on the place value chart to represent the following equations. Write the product in standard form.

(5 ten thousands 3 thousands) × 10 = <u>530,000</u>

How many thousands are in your answer? <u>530 *thousands*</u>

> The place value to the left represents 10 times as much, so I can draw an arrow and label it "× 10".

millions	hundred thousands	ten thousands	thousands	hundreds	tens	ones
		●●●●● ● × 10	●●● ● × 10			
	●●●●● ●	●●●				

> 3 ten thousands is 10 times more than 3 thousands. 5 hundred thousands is 10 times more than 5 ten thousands. So, (5 ten thousands 3 thousands) × 10 is 530,000.

Lesson 3: Name numbers within 1 million by building understanding of the place value chart and placement of commas for naming base thousand units.

EUREKA MATH

G4-M1-Lesson 4

1.

   a. On the place value chart below, label the units, and represent the number 43,082.

millions	hundred thousands	ten thousands	thousands	hundreds	tens	ones
		●●●●	●●●		●●●●● ●●●	●●

   b. Write the number in word form.   *forty-three thousand, eighty-two*

> I read 43,082 to myself. I write the words that I say. I add commas to separate the periods of thousands and ones, just as I do when I write numerals.

   c. Write the number in expanded form. $40,000 + 3,000 + 80 + 2$

> I write the value of each digit in 43,082 as an addition expression. The 4 has a value of 4 ten thousands, which I write in standard form as 40,000. $43,082 = 40,000 + 3,000 + 80 + 2$.

EUREKA MATH   **Lesson 4:**   Read and write multi digit numbers using base ten numerals, number na and expanded form.   7

©2015 Great Minds. eureka-math.org
G4-M1-HWH-1.3.0-07.2015

2. Use pictures, numbers, and words to explain another way to say 39 hundred.

Another way to say 39 hundred is 3 thousand, 9 hundred. I can write 3,900, and I draw 39 hundreds disks as 3 thousands disks and 9 hundreds disks.

millions	hundred thousands	ten thousands	thousands	hundreds	tens	ones

I know 10 hundreds is the same as 1 thousand. I can bundle 30 hundreds to make 3 thousands.

Lesson 4:   Read and write multi-digit numbers using base ten numerals, number na and expanded form.

©2015 Great Minds. eureka-math.org
G4-M1-HWH-1.3.0-07.2015

G4-M1-Lesson 5

1. Label the units in the place value chart. Draw place value disks to represent each number in the place value chart. Use <, >, or = to compare the two numbers. Write the correct symbol in the circle.

503,421 ⟨ > ⟩ 350,491

> I record the comparison symbol for *greater than*.

millions	hundred thousands	ten thousands	thousands	hundreds	tens	ones
	●●●●●		●●●	●●●●	●●	●
	●●●	●●●●●		●●●●	●●●●● ●●●●	●

> I record the value of each digit using place value disks, placing 503,421 in the top half and 350,491 in the bottom half of the place value chart. I can clearly see and compare the unit with the greatest value—hundred thousands. 5 hundred thousands is greater than 3 hundred thousands. 503,421 is greater than 350,491.

2. Compare the two numbers by using the symbols <, >, or =. Write the correct symbol in the circle.

six hundred two thousand, four hundred seventy-three ⟨ < ⟩ 600,000 + 50,000 + 2,000 + 700 + 7

> It helps me to solve if I write both numbers in standard form.

602,473 ⟨ < ⟩ 652,707

> Since the value of the largest unit is the same, I compare the next largest unit—the ten thousands. Zero ten thousands is less than five ten thousands. So, 602,473 is less than 652,707. I record the comparison symbol for *less than* to complete my answer.

Lesson 5:   Compare numbers based on meanings of the digits using <, >, or = to rec
comparison.

9

©2015 Great Minds. eureka-math.org
G4-M1-HWH-1.3.0-07.2015

3. Jill has $1,462, Adam has $1,509, Cristina has $1,712, and Robin has $1,467. Arrange the amounts of money in order from greatest to least. Then, name who has the most money.

thousands	hundreds	tens	ones
1	4	6	2
1	5	0	9
1	7	1	2
1	4	6	7

Listing the amounts of money in a place value chart helps me to see the values in each unit.

$$\$1,712 > \$1,509 > \$1,467 > \$1,462$$

Cristina has the most money.

I notice 1,462 and 1,467 both have 1 thousand, 4 hundreds, *and* 6 tens. So, I compare the ones. 7 ones is more than 2 ones. 1,467 is greater than 1,462.

10   **Lesson 5:**   Compare numbers based on meanings of the digits using <, >, or = to rec
                              comparison.

©2015 Great Minds. eureka-math.org
G4-M1-HWH-1.3.0-07.2015

EUREKA MATH

G4-M1-Lesson 6

1. Label the place value chart. Use place value disks to find the sum or difference. Write the answer in standard form on the line.

   a. 100,000 less than six hundred thirty thousand, five hundred seventeen is _____ 530,517 _____.

millions	hundred thousands	ten thousands	thousands	hundreds	tens	ones
	●●●●● ✗	●●●		●●●●●	●	●●●●● ●●

   > After modeling 630,517, I cross off 1 hundred thousand disk. 100,000 less than 630,517 is 530,517.

   b. 260,993 is **10,000 more** than 250,993.

millions	hundred thousands	ten thousands	thousands	hundreds	tens	ones
	●●	●●●●● Ⓞ		●●●●● ●●●●	●●●●● ●●●●	●●●

   > To model 260,993 in comparison to 250,993, I add 1 ten thousand disk. 60,000 is 10,000 more than 50,000. Therefore, 260,993 is 10,000 more than 250,993.

2. Fill in the blank for this equation:

   17,082 – 1,000 = _____ 16,082 _____.

   > There are 17 thousands in 17,082. 1 thousand less than 17 thousand is 16 thousands.

3. Fill in the boxes to complete the patterns. Explain in pictures, numbers, or words how you found your answers.

245,975	345,975	445,975	545,975	645,975	745,975

Student Response 1:

I see that the hundred thousand unit increases. The other units remain the same. In the first number, there are 2 hundred thousands. Then, there are 4 hundred thousands and 6 hundred thousands. I can fill in the boxes with 3 hundred thousands, 5 hundred thousands, and 7 hundred thousands. Each number in the pattern increases by 1 hundred thousand each time.

I answer the question, "Are the numbers in the pattern growing or shrinking? By how much?"

Student Response 2:

The numbers increase by 100,000 each time.

hundred thousands	ten thousands	thousands	hundreds	tens	ones
2	4	5	9	7	5
3	4	5	9	7	5
4	4	5	9	7	5
5	4	5	9	7	5
6	4	5	9	7	5
7	4	5	9	7	5

$245,975 + 100,000 = 345,975$

$345,975 + 100,000 = 445,975$

$445,975 + 100,000 = 545,975$

$545,975 + 100,000 = 645,975$

$645,975 + 100,000 = 745,975$

I quickly write numerals instead of number disks. I can see clearly that the hundred thousands increase. The other values don't change.

I write a series of number sentences to show the same change each time. The rule of the pattern is "add 100,000."

EUREKA
MATH

G4-M1-Lesson 7

1. Round to the nearest thousand. Use the number line to model your thinking.

   a. $3,941 \approx$ $4,000$ b. $53,269 \approx$ $53,000$

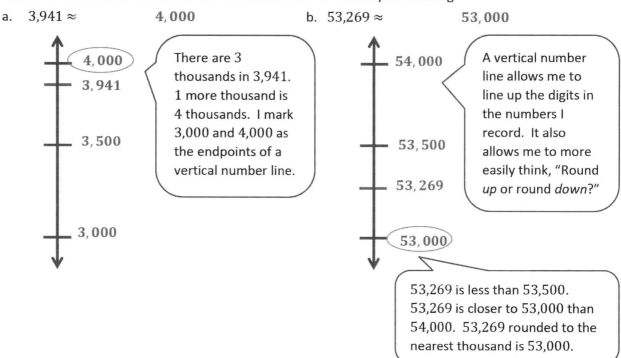

There are 3 thousands in 3,941. 1 more thousand is 4 thousands. I mark 3,000 and 4,000 as the endpoints of a vertical number line.

A vertical number line allows me to line up the digits in the numbers I record. It also allows me to more easily think, "Round *up* or round *down*?"

53,269 is less than 53,500. 53,269 is closer to 53,000 than 54,000. 53,269 rounded to the nearest thousand is 53,000.

2. In 2013, the family vacation cost $3,809. In 2014, the family vacation cost $4,699. The family budgeted about $4,000 for each vacation. In which year did the family stay closer to their budget? Round to the nearest thousand. Use what you know about place value to explain your answer.

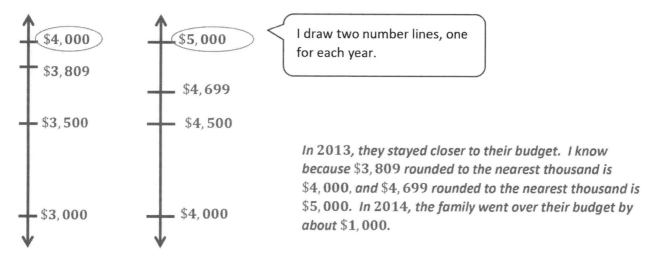

I draw two number lines, one for each year.

In 2013, they stayed closer to their budget. I know because $3,809 rounded to the nearest thousand is $4,000, and $4,699 rounded to the nearest thousand is $5,000. In 2014, the family went over their budget by about $1,000.

G4-M1-Lesson 8

1. Complete each statement by rounding the number to the given place value. Use the number line to show your work.

   a. 41,899 rounded to the nearest ten thousand is   40,000

   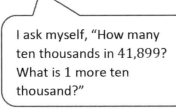 I ask myself, "How many ten thousands in 41,899? What is 1 more ten thousand?"

   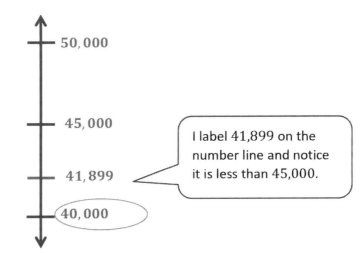

   I label 41,899 on the number line and notice it is less than 45,000.

   b. 267,072 rounded to the nearest hundred thousand is   300,000

   I know that there are 2 hundred thousands in 267,072. One more hundred thousand is 3 hundred thousands.

   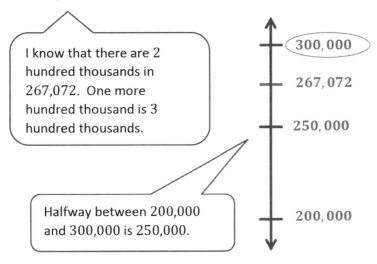

   Halfway between 200,000 and 300,000 is 250,000.

Lesson 8:   Round multi-digit numbers to any place using the vertical number line.

©2015 Great Minds. eureka-math.org
G4-M1-HWH-1.3.0-07.2015

2. 982,510 books were downloaded in one year. Round this number to the nearest hundred thousand to estimate how many books were downloaded in one year. Use a number line to show your work.

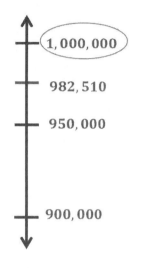

There are 9 hundred thousands in 982,510. 1 more hundred thousand is 10 hundred thousands, or 1 million. I label my endpoints 900,000 and 1,000,000. Halfway is 950,000.

About 1 million books were downloaded in one year.

3. Estimate the difference by rounding each number to the given place value.

$$519,240 - 339,705$$

a. Round to the nearest hundred thousand.

$$500,000 - 300,000 = 200,000$$

b. Round to the nearest ten thousand.

$$520,000 - 340,000 = 180,000$$

Thinking in unit language makes this subtraction easy: 520 thousands minus 340 thousands equals 180 thousands.

G4-M1-Lesson 9

1. Round to the nearest thousand.

    a. $7,598 \approx$ _____ $8,000$ _____

    > I remember from Lesson 7 how to round to the nearest thousand.

    b. $301,409 \approx$ _____ $301,000$ _____

    c. Explain how you found your answer for Part (b).

    There are 301 thousands in $301,409$. One more thousand is 302 thousands. Halfway between 301 thousands and 302 thousands is 301 thousands 5 hundreds. $301,409$ is less than $301,500$. Therefore, $301,409$ rounded to the nearest thousand is $301,000$.

2. Round to the nearest ten thousand.

    a. $73,999 \approx$ _____ $70,000$ _____

    > I may need to draw a number line to verify my answer.

    b. $65,002 \approx$ _____ $70,000$ _____

    c. Explain why the two problems have the same answer. Write another number that has the same answer when rounded to the nearest ten thousand.

    Any number equal to or greater than $65,000$ and less than $75,000$ will round to $70,000$ when rounded to the nearest ten thousand. $65,002$ is greater than $65,000$, and $73,999$ is less than $75,000$. Another number that would round to $70,000$ is $68,234$.

Lesson 9:   Use place value understanding to round multi digit numbers to any place   **EUREKA MATH**

©2015 Great Minds. eureka-math.org
G4-M1-HWH-1.3.0-07.2015

Solve the following problems using pictures, numbers, or words.

3. About 700,000 people make up the population of Americatown. If the population was rounded to the nearest hundred thousand, what could be the greatest and least number of people who make up the population of Americatown?

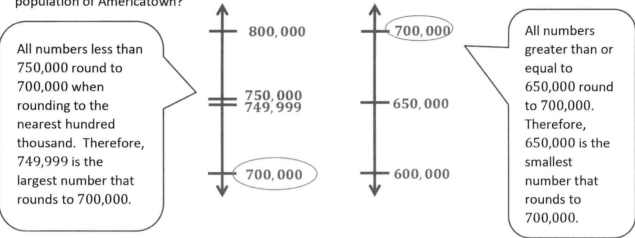

The greatest number of people that could make up the population is $749,999$. *I know because it is* 1 *fewer than* $750,000$. *The least number of people that could make up the population is* $650,000$.

G4-M1-Lesson 10

1. Round 745,001 to the nearest

    > I remember from Lesson 7 to ask myself, "Between what two thousands is 745,001?" I try to picture the number line in my head.

    a. thousand: _____745,000_____

    b. ten thousand: _____750,000_____

    > I remember from Lesson 8 to find how many ten thousands and how many hundred thousands are in 745,001. Then, add one more of that unit to find the endpoints.

    c. hundred thousand: _____700,000_____

Solve the following problem using pictures, numbers, or words.

2. 37,248 people subscribe to the delivery of a local newspaper. To decide about how many papers to print, what place value should 37,248 be rounded to so each person receives a copy? Explain.

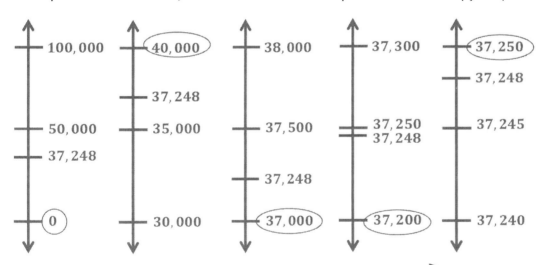

37,248 should be rounded to the nearest ten thousand or the nearest ten. Extra papers will be printed, but if I round to the nearest hundred thousand, thousand, or hundred, there won't be enough papers printed.

> Drawing number lines helps to prove my written answer.

Lesson 10:   Use place value understanding to round multi digit numbers to any place
                      using real world applications.

G4-M1-Lesson 11

Using an algorithm means that the steps repeat themselves unit by unit. It can be an efficient way to solve a

1. Solve the addition problems using the standard algorithm.

a.
```
    5,  1  2  2
 +  2,  4  5  7
 ──────────────
    7,  5  7  9
```

b.
```
    5,  1  2  4
 +  2,  4  5  7
 ──────────────
           1
    7,  5  8  1
```

c. $38,192 + 6,387 + 241,458$
```
       3  8,  1  9  2
           6,  3  8  7
 +   2  4  1,  4  5  8
 ──────────────────────
           1  1  2  1
    2  8  6,  0  3  7
```

No regroupings here! I just add like units. 2 ones plus 7 ones is 9 ones. I put the 9 in the ones column as part of the sum. Then, I continue to add the number of units of tens, the hundreds, and the thousands.

I have to regroup ones. 4 ones + 7 ones = 11 ones. 11 ones equals 1 ten 1 one. I record 1 ten in the tens place on the line. I record 1 one in the ones column as part of the sum.

The order of the addends doesn't matter as long as like units are lined up.

I add tens. 2 tens + 5 tens + 1 ten = 8 tens. I record 8 tens in the tens column as part of the sum.

2. Draw a tape diagram to represent the problem. Use numbers to solve, and write your answer as a statement.

In July, the ice cream stand sold some ice cream cones. 3,907 were vanilla. 2,568 were not vanilla. How many cones did they sell in July?

I can draw a tape diagram. I know the two parts, but I don't know the whole. I can label the unknown with a variable, C.

I write an equation. Then, I solve to find the total. I write a statement to tell my answer.

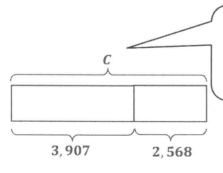

$$3,907 + 2,568 = C$$

```
    3,  9  0  7
 +  2,  5  6  8
 ──────────────
        1     1
    6,  4  7  5
```

The ice cream stand sold 6,475 cones in July.

EUREKA MATH   Lesson 11:   Use place value understanding to fluently add multi-digit whole numbers
                                       using the standard addition algorithm, and apply the algorithm to solve
                                       word problems using tape diagrams.   **19**

©2015 Great Minds. eureka-math.org
G4-M1-HWH-1.3.0-07.2015

G4-M1-Lesson 12

Estimate and then solve. Model the problem with a tape diagram. Explain if your answer is reasonable.

1. There were 4,806 more visitors to the zoo in the month of July than in the month of June. June had 6,782 visitors. How many visitors did the zoo have during both months?

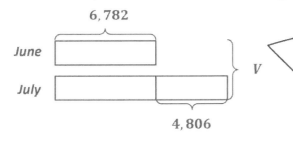

6,782

June

July

V

4,806

Since the problem states the relationship between June and July, I can draw two tapes. I make July's tape longer because there were more visitors in July. I partition July's tape into two parts: one part for the number of people in June and the other part for 4,806 more visitors.

a. About how many visitors did the zoo have during June and July?

$7,000 + 7,000 + 5,000 = 19,000$

The zoo had about 19,000 visitors during June and July.

To estimate the total, I round each number to the nearest thousand and add those numbers together.

b. Exactly how many visitors did the zoo have during June and July?

```
     6,  7   8   2
     6,  7   8   2
  +  4,  8   0   6
  ─────2───1───1──
  1  8,  3   7   0
```

When I look at my tape diagram, I see that I don't have to solve for July to find the total. This saves me a step.

The zoo had exactly 18,370 visitors during June and July.

c. Is your answer reasonable? Compare your estimate to the answer. Write a sentence to explain your reasoning.

Sample Response: My answer is reasonable because my estimate of 19,000 is only about 600 more than the actual answer of 18,370. My estimate is greater than the actual answer because I rounded each addend up to the next thousand.

Lesson 12:   Solve multi-step word problems using the standard addition algorithm modeled with tape diagrams, and assess the reasonableness of answers using rounding.

EUREKA
MATH

2. Emma's class spent four months collecting pennies.

   a. During Month 3, the class collected 1,211 more pennies than they did during Month 2. Find the total number of pennies collected in four months.

Month	Pennies Collected
1	4,987
2	8,709
3	
4	8,192

Month 1 [4,987]

Month 2 [8,709] 1,211

Month 3 [8,709][ ]   } *P*

Month 4 [8,192]

> I draw four tapes to represent each month. Now, I can see how many pennies were collected in Month 3.

$5,000 + 9,000 + 9,000 + 1,000 + 8,000 = 32,000$

```
    4,  9  8  7
    8,  7  0  9
    8,  7  0  9
    1,  2  1  1
+   8,  1  9  2
    2   2  2
  ─────────────
  3 1,  8  0  8
```

> I add in unit form: 5 thousands + 9 thousands + 9 thousands + 1 thousand + 8 thousands = 32 thousands. 32 thousand is an estimate of the total number of pennies collected in four months.

The total number of pennies collected in four months was 31,808.

> To find the total pennies collected in the four months, I could solve for Month 3 and then add all of the months together to solve for *P*. Instead, I just add the value of each of the tapes together. The tape diagram shows me how to solve this in one step, not two.

   b. Is your answer reasonable? Explain.

   Sample Response: My answer is reasonable. 31,808 is only about 200 less than the estimate of 32,000.

Lesson 12: Solve multi-step word problems using the standard addition algorithm modeled with tape diagrams, and assess the reasonableness of answers using rounding.   21

©2015 Great Minds. eureka-math.org
G4-M1-HWH-1.3.0-07.2015

G4-M1-Lesson 13

> I don't have enough tens to subtract 5 tens from 3 tens. I decompose 1 hundred for 10 tens.

1. Use the standard algorithm to solve the following subtraction problems.

a.
```
   6, 5 6 7
 - 1, 4 5 7
   5, 1 1 0
```

b.
```
        4  13
   6, 5̶  3̶  7
 - 2, 4  5  7
   4, 0  8  0
```

> I look across the top number to see if I can subtract. I have enough units, so no regroupings! I just subtract like units. 7 ones minus 7 ones is 0 ones. I continue to subtract the number of units of tens, hundreds, and thousands.

> Now, I have 4 hundreds. I show this by crossing off the 5 and writing a 4 in the hundreds place instead. 10 tens + 3 tens = 13 tens. I show this by crossing off the 3 tens and writing 13 in the tens place instead.

c. 3,532 – 921

```
   2  15
   3̶, 5̶  3  2
 -     9  2  1
   2,  6  1  1
```

> Just like in Lesson 11, I write the problem in vertical form, being sure to line up the units.

2. What number must be added to 23,165 to result in a sum of 46,884?

> To solve a word problem, I use RDW: Read, Draw, Write. I read the problem. I draw a picture, like a tape diagram, and I write my answer as an equation and a statement.

$$23,165 + n = 46,884$$

46,884
```
| 23,165 | n |
```

```
          7  14
   4 6, 8  8̶  4̶
 - 2 3, 1  6  5
   2 3, 7  1  9
```

23,719 *must be added to* 23,165.

Lesson 13: Use place value understanding to decompose to smaller units once using the standard subtraction algorithm, and apply the algorithm to solve word problems using tape diagrams.

EUREKA MATH

©2015 Great Minds. eureka-math.org
G4-M1-HWH-1.3.0-07.2015

Draw a tape diagram to model the problem. Use numbers to solve, and write your answer as a statement. Check your answer.

3. Mr. Swanson drove his car 5,654 miles. Mrs. Swanson drove her car some miles, too. If they drove 11,965 miles combined, how many miles did Mrs. Swanson drive?

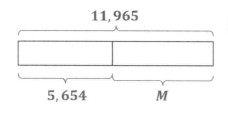

$11,965 - 5,654 = M$

```
    0   11
    1   1,  9   6   5
 -      5,  6   5   4
        6,  3   1   1
```

```
        6,  3   1   1
 +      5,  6   5   4
     1  1,  9   6   5
```

Mrs. Swanson drove 6,311 miles.

To check my answer, I add the difference to the known part. It equals the whole, so I subtracted correctly.

Lesson 13: Use place value understanding to decompose to smaller units once using the standard subtraction algorithm, and apply the algorithm to solve word problems using tape diagrams.

©2015 Great Minds. eureka-math.org
G4-M1-HWH-1.3.0-07.2015

G4-M1-Lesson 14

1. Use the standard algorithm to solve the following subtraction problems.

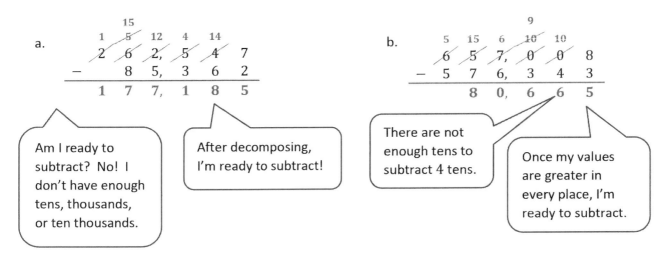

a.

$$\begin{array}{cccccc} 1 & \overset{15}{\cancel{5}} & 12 & 4 & 14 & \\ \cancel{2} & \cancel{6} & \cancel{2}, & \cancel{5} & \cancel{4} & 7 \\ - & & 8 & 5, & 3 & 6 & 2 \\ \hline & 1 & 7 & 7, & 1 & 8 & 5 \end{array}$$

Am I ready to subtract? No! I don't have enough tens, thousands, or ten thousands.

After decomposing, I'm ready to subtract!

b.

$$\begin{array}{cccccc} & & & 9 & & \\ 5 & 15 & 6 & \cancel{10} & 10 & \\ \cancel{6} & \cancel{5} & \cancel{7}, & \cancel{0} & \cancel{0} & 8 \\ - & 5 & 7 & 6, & 3 & 4 & 3 \\ \hline & 8 & 0, & 6 & 6 & 5 \end{array}$$

There are not enough tens to subtract 4 tens.

Once my values are greater in every place, I'm ready to subtract.

Draw a tape diagram to represent the following problem. Use numbers to solve, and write your answer as a statement. Check your answer.

2. Stella had 542,000 visits to her website. Raquel had 231,348 visits to her website. How many more visits did Stella have than Raquel?

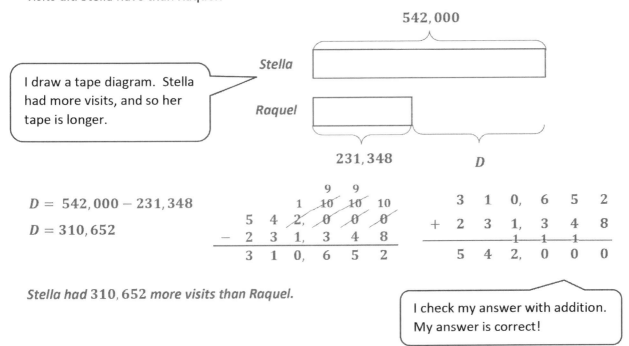

I draw a tape diagram. Stella had more visits, and so her tape is longer.

542,000

Stella

Raquel

231,348   D

$D = 542,000 - 231,348$

$D = 310,652$

$$\begin{array}{cccccc} & & 9 & 9 & & \\ & 1 & \cancel{10} & \cancel{10} & 10 & \\ 5 & 4 & \cancel{2}, & \cancel{0} & \cancel{0} & \cancel{0} \\ - 2 & 3 & 1, & 3 & 4 & 8 \\ \hline 3 & 1 & 0, & 6 & 5 & 2 \end{array}$$

$$\begin{array}{cccccc} 3 & 1 & 0, & 6 & 5 & 2 \\ + 2 & 3 & 1, & 3 & 4 & 8 \\ & & & 1 & 1 & 1 \\ \hline 5 & 4 & 2, & 0 & 0 & 0 \end{array}$$

Stella had 310,652 more visits than Raquel.

I check my answer with addition. My answer is correct!

Lesson 14: Use place value understanding to decompose to smaller units up to three times using the standard subtraction algorithm, and apply the algorithm to solve word problems using tape diagrams

EUREKA MATH™

©2015 Great Minds. eureka-math.org
G4-M1-HWH-1.3.0-07.2015

G4-M1-Lesson 15

Use the standard subtraction algorithm to solve the problem below.

1.
```
    6   0   0,   4   0   0
  −     7   2,   6   4   9
```

I am not ready to subtract. I must regroup.

Sample Student A Response:

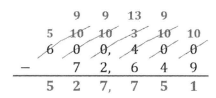

I work unit by unit, starting with the ones. I can rename 4 hundreds as 3 hundreds 10 tens. Then, I rename 10 tens as 9 tens 10 ones. I'll continue to decompose until I am ready to subtract.

Sample Student B Response:

```
                13
    5   9   9   3   9   10
  − 6   0   0,  4   0   0
        7   2,  6   4   9
    5   2   7,  7   5   1
```

I need more ones. I unbundle 40 tens as 39 tens 10 ones.

I need more than 3 hundreds to subtract 6 hundreds. I can rename the 600 thousands as 599 thousands 10 hundreds. 10 hundreds plus 3 hundreds is 13 hundreds.

EUREKA MATH

Lesson 15: Use place value understanding to fluently decompose to smaller units multiple times in any place using the standard subtraction algorithm, and apply the algorithm to solve word problems using tape diagrams.

25

©2015 Great Minds. eureka-math.org
G4-M1-HWH-1.3.0-07.2015

Use a tape diagram and the standard algorithm to solve the problem below. Check your answer.

2. The cost of the Johnston's new home was $200,000. They paid for most of it and now owe $33,562. How much have they already paid?

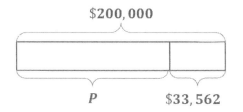

$200,000 - $33,562 = P$

Sample Student A Response:

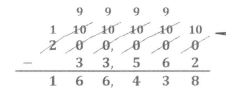

There are a lot of decompositions!

Sample Student B Response:

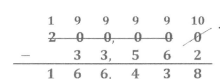

I rename 20,000 tens as 19,999 tens 10 ones.

```
    1   6   6,   4   3   8
+       3   3,   5   6   2
    1   1    1   1   1
    2   0   0,   0   0   0
```

I check my answer by adding the two parts. The sum is equal to the cost of the new home. My answer is correct!

The Johnstons have already paid $166,438.

Lesson 15: Use place value understanding to fluently decompose to smaller units multiple times in any place using the standard subtraction algorithm, and apply the algorithm to solve word problems using tape diagrams.

EUREKA
MATH™

G4-M1-Lesson 16

1. In its three months of summer business, the local ice cream stand had a total of $94,326 in sales. The first month's sales were $24,314, and the second month's sales were $30,867.

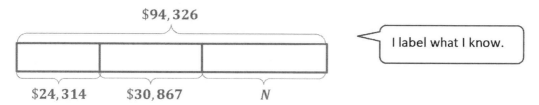

$94,326

$24,314 $30,867   N

I label what I know.

a. Round each value to the nearest ten thousand to estimate the sales of the third month.

$24,314 \approx $20,000$ $20,000 + $30,000 = $50,000$

$30,867 \approx $30,000$ $90,000 - $50,000 = $40,000$

$94,326 \approx $90,000$ *The sales of the third month were about* $40,000.

To estimate the sales of the third month, I subtract the sum from two months from the total amount.

b. Find the exact amount of sales of the third month.

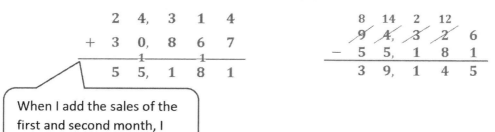

When I add the sales of the first and second month, I regroup on the line.

The exact amount of sales of the third month was $39,145.

c. Use your answer from part (a) to explain why your answer in part (b) is reasonable.

My answer of $39,145 *is reasonable because it is close to my estimate of* $40,000. *The difference between the actual answer and my estimate is less than* $1,000.

EUREKA MATH   **Lesson 16:** Solve two-step word problems using the standard subtraction algorithm fluently modeled with tape diagrams, and assess the reasonableness of answers using rounding.   27

©2015 Great Minds. eureka-math.org
G4-M1-HWH-1.3.0-07.2015

2. In the first month after its release, 55,316 copies of a best-selling book were sold. In the second month after its release, 16,427 fewer copies were sold. How many copies were sold in the first two months? Is your answer reasonable?

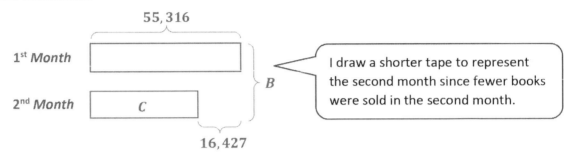

55,316

1st Month

2nd Month   C

B

I draw a shorter tape to represent the second month since fewer books were sold in the second month.

16,427

Sample Student A Response:

$C = 55,316 - 16,427$

$C = 38,889$

I subtract to find the actual number of copies sold in the second month.

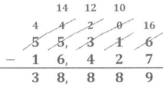

$$\begin{array}{r} 14 \ \ 12 \ \ 10 \\ 4 \ \ \ 4 \ \ \ 2 \ \ \ 0 \ \ 16 \\ 5 \ \ 5, \ 3 \ \ 1 \ \ 6 \\ - \ 1 \ \ 6, \ 4 \ \ 2 \ \ 7 \\ \hline 3 \ \ 8, \ 8 \ \ 8 \ \ 9 \end{array}$$

Then, I add the number of copies of the first and second month together to find the total.

$B = 55,316 + 38,889$

$B = 94,205$

$$\begin{array}{r} 5 \ \ 5, \ 3 \ \ 1 \ \ 6 \\ + \ 3 \ \ 8, \ 8 \ \ 8 \ \ 9 \\ \hline 1 \ 1 \ \ 1 \ \ 1 \\ 9 \ \ 4, \ 2 \ \ 0 \ \ 5 \end{array}$$

$55,316 \approx 60,000$

$16,427 \approx 20,000$

$60,000 - 20,000 = 40,000$

$60,000 + 40,000 = 100,000$

Sample Student B Response:

$B = 55,316 + 55,316 - 16,427$

$B = 110,632 - 16,427$

$B = 94,205$

To find the total number copies I can add two units of 55,316 and then subtract 16,427.

$$\begin{array}{r} 5 \ \ 5, \ 3 \ \ 1 \ \ 6 \\ + \ 5 \ \ 5, \ 3 \ \ 1 \ \ 6 \\ \hline 1 \ \ \ \ \ \ \ 1 \\ 1 \ 1 \ \ 0, \ 6 \ \ 3 \ \ 2 \end{array}$$

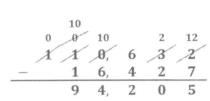

$$\begin{array}{r} 10 \\ 0 \ \ 0 \ \ 10 \ \ \ \ 2 \ \ 12 \\ 1 \ \ 1 \ \ 0, \ 6 \ \ 3 \ \ 2 \\ - \ \ \ \ \ 1 \ \ 6, \ 4 \ \ 2 \ \ 7 \\ \hline 9 \ \ 4, \ 2 \ \ 0 \ \ 5 \end{array}$$

$110,632 \approx 111,000$

$16,427 \approx 16,000$

$111,000 - 16,000 = 95,000$

94,205 *copies were sold in the first two months.*

I round to the nearest ten thousand. My answer is reasonable. It is about 6,000 less than my estimate. I would expect this difference because I rounded each number *up* to the nearest ten thousand.

I round to the nearest thousand. My answer is really close to my estimate! When I round to a smaller place value unit, I often get an estimate closer to the actual answer.

Lesson 16: Solve two step word problems using the standard subtraction algorithm fluently modeled with tape diagrams, and assess the reasonableness of answers using rounding.

EUREKA MATH™

G4-M1-Lesson 17

Draw a tape diagram to represent each problem. Use numbers to solve, and write your answer as a statement.

1. Saisha has 1,025 stickers. Evan only has 862 stickers. How many more stickers does Saisha have than Evan?

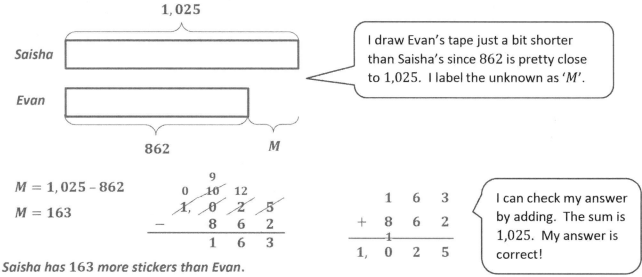

I draw Evan's tape just a bit shorter than Saisha's since 862 is pretty close to 1,025. I label the unknown as 'M'.

$M = 1,025 - 862$

$M = 163$

I can check my answer by adding. The sum is 1,025. My answer is correct!

Saisha has 163 more stickers than Evan.

2. Milk Truck B contains 3,994 gallons of milk. Together, Milk Truck A and Milk Truck B contain 8,789 gallons of milk. How many more gallons of milk does Milk Truck A contain than Milk Truck B?

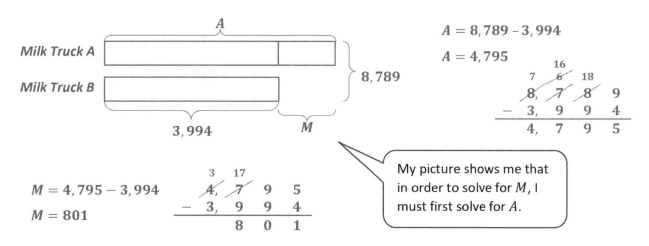

$A = 8,789 - 3,994$

$A = 4,795$

$M = 4,795 - 3,994$

$M = 801$

My picture shows me that in order to solve for M, I must first solve for A.

Milk Truck A contains 801 more gallons of milk than Milk Truck B.

3. The length of the purple streamer measured 180 inches. After 40 inches were cut from it, the purple streamer was twice as long as the blue streamer. At first, how many inches longer was the purple streamer than the blue streamer?

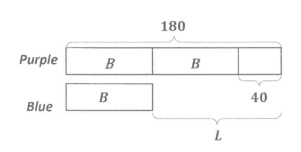

> I use unit language to help me solve. The purple streamer is now 140 inches long.

$2B = 18 \text{ tens} - 4 \text{ tens}$

$2B = 14 \text{ tens or } 140$

$B = 14 \text{ tens} \div 2$

$B = 7 \text{ tens}$

$B = 70$

> I divide to find the length of the blue streamer.

$L = 180 - 70$

$L = 18 \text{ tens} - 7 \text{ tens}$

$L = 11 \text{ tens}$

$L = 110$

At first, the purple streamer was 110 inches longer than the blue streamer.

> I subtract the length of the blue streamer from the original length of the purple streamer.

EUREKA MATH

©2015 Great Minds. eureka-math.org
G4-M1-HWH-1.3.0-07.2015

G4-M1-Lesson 18

Draw a tape diagram to represent each problem. Use numbers to solve, and write your answer as a statement.

1. Bridget wrote down three numbers. The first number was 7,401. The second number was 4,610 less than the first. The third number was 2,842 greater than the second. What is the sum of her numbers?

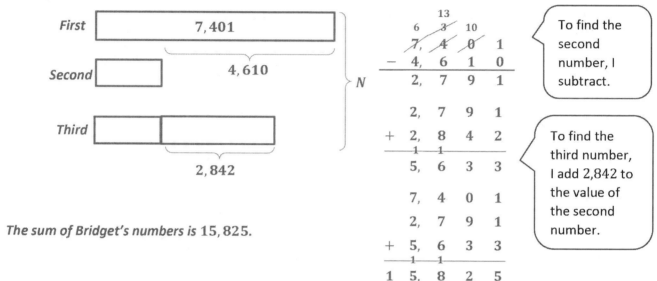

The sum of Bridget's numbers is 15,825.

To find the second number, I subtract.

To find the third number, I add 2,842 to the value of the second number.

2. Mrs. Sample sold a total of 43,210 pounds of mulch. She sold 13,305 pounds of cherry mulch. She sold 4,617 more pounds of birch mulch than cherry. The rest of the mulch sold was maple. How many pounds of maple mulch were sold?

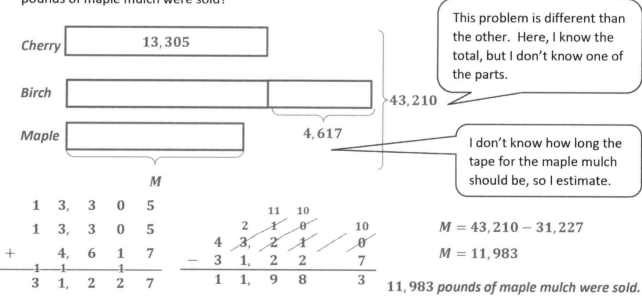

This problem is different than the other. Here, I know the total, but I don't know one of the parts.

I don't know how long the tape for the maple mulch should be, so I estimate.

$M = 43,210 - 31,227$

$M = 11,983$

11,983 pounds of maple mulch were sold.

EUREKA MATH

Lesson 18: Solve multi-step word problems modeled with tape diagrams, and assess the reasonableness of answers using rounding.

31

©2015 Great Minds. eureka-math.org
G4-M1-HWH-1.3.0-07.2015

G4-M1-Lesson 19

1. Using the diagram below, create your own word problem. Solve for the value of the variable, T.

There are 28,596 _people who work for_

Company A. There are 26,325 more _people_

who work for Company B than Company A.

How many _people work for the two companies in_

all ?

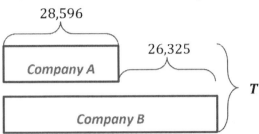

> After analyzing the tape diagram, I create a context for a word problem and fill in the blanks. I write "how many in all" because the total, T, is unknown.

Company B = 28,596 + 26,325 T = Company A + Company B

```
    2  8,  5  9  6              5  4,  9  2  1
 +  2  6,  3  2  5           +  2  8,  5  9  6
    ─1──────1──1──              ─1──1──1───────
    5  4,  9  2  1              8  3,  5  1  7
```

83,517 people work for the two companies in all.

2. Use the following tape diagram to create a word problem. Solve for the value of the variable, A.

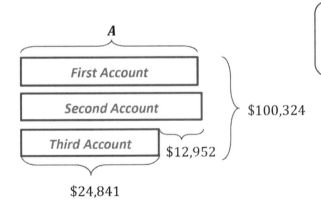

> I analyze the tape diagram. I find a context, and write a word problem based on what is known and what is unknown. I label the parts.

Mr. W had 3 bank accounts with a total balance of $100,324. He had $24,841 in his third account and $12,952 more in his second account than in his third account. What was the balance of Mr. W's first account?

```
   1  2,  9  5  2         3  7,  7  9  3              9  9
 + 2  4,  8  4  1       + 2  4,  8  4  1            1̶0̶ 1̶0̶ 12  12
   ───────1─────          ──1──1──1─────        1  0̶  0̶,  3̶  2̶  4
   3  7,  7  9  3         6  2,  6  3  4        ─  6  2,  6  3  4
                                                  3  7,  6  9  0
```

Mr. W's first account had a balance of $37,690.

Lesson 19:   Create and solve multi-step word problems from given tape diagrams and
                             equations.

EUREKA
MATH

Homework Helpers

Grade 4
Module 2

G4-M2-Lesson 1

1. Find the equivalent measures.

    a. 3 km = ___3,000___ m   b. 4 m = ___400___ cm

    > I know that 1 kilometer equals 1,000 meters.

    > I know that 1 meter equals 100 centimeters.

2. Find the equivalent measures.

    a. 2 km 345 m = ___2,345___ m   b. 4 m 23 cm = ___423___ cm

    c. 12 km 45 m = ___12,045___ m   d. 24 m 3 cm = ___2,403___ cm

    > I know that 12 kilometers equals 12,000 meters, so I add 12,000 meters plus 45 meters.

    > I know that 24 meters equals 2,400 centimeters, so I add 2,400 meters plus 3 centimeters.

3. Solve.

    a. 3 m – 42 cm

    Sample Student A Response:

    $$3\ m\ =\ 300\ cm$$

    ```
          2  9  10
         3̶  0̶  0̶   cm
       −    4  2   cm
       ─────────────
         2  5  8   cm
    ```

    Sample Student B Response:

    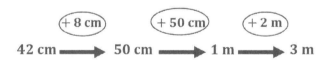

    $$8\ cm + 50\ cm + 2\ m = 2\ m\ 58\ cm$$

    > Before subtracting, I make like units. 3 meters is equal to 300 centimeters.

    > I'll use the arrow way to add up. I add centimeters and meters that make the next whole.

    > I add 8 cm to make the next ten, 50 cm. I add 50 cm to make the next meter, and 1 meter is 2 meters away from 3 meters.

    > Now I'll add all the parts circled, finding 2 meters 58 centimeters is the difference of 3 meters and 42 centimeters.

Lesson 1:   Express metric length measurements in terms of a smaller unit; model and
            solve addition and subtraction word problems involving metric length.

1

b. 32 m 14 cm − 8 m 63 cm

Sample Student A Response:

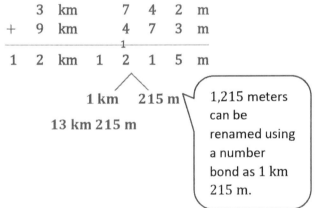

```
    2  11     0  11
    3   1     1   1   4
    3   2  m  1   4   cm
 −      8  m     6  3   cm
 ──────────────────────────
    2   3  m     5  1   cm
```

14 cm is not enough to take away 63 cm, so I rename 1 meter as 100 cm to make 114 cm.

Sample Student B Response:

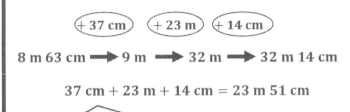

(+ 37 cm) (+ 23 m) (+ 14 cm)

8 m 63 cm ➡ 9 m ➡ 32 m ➡ 32 m 14 cm

37 cm + 23 m + 14 cm = 23 m 51 cm

Using the arrow way, I'll add up from 8 m 63 cm until I reach 32 m 14 cm. It's almost like a number line!

c. 3 km 742 m + 9 km 473 m

Sample Student A Response:

```
    3  km     7  4  2  m
 +  9  km     4  7  3  m
 ──────────────────────────
            1
 1  2  km  1  2  1  5  m
```

1 km   215 m

13 km 215 m

1,215 meters can be renamed using a number bond as 1 km 215 m.

Sample Student B Response:

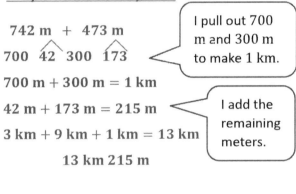

742 m + 473 m

700 42 300 173

700 m + 300 m = 1 km

42 m + 173 m = 215 m

3 km + 9 km + 1 km = 13 km

13 km 215 m

I pull out 700 m and 300 m to make 1 km.

I add the remaining meters.

Use a tape diagram to model each problem. Solve using a simplifying strategy or an algorithm, and write your answer as a statement.

4. Kya's mom drove 4 km 231 m from work to the grocery store. She drove some more miles from the grocery store to her house. If she drove a total of 8 km, how far was it from her work to her house?

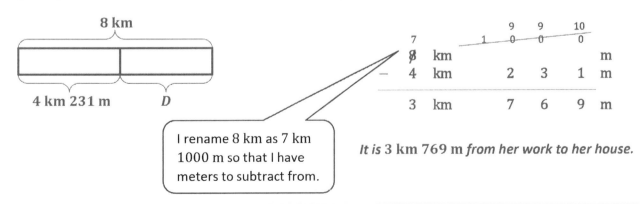

8 km

4 km 231 m   D

I rename 8 km as 7 km 1000 m so that I have meters to subtract from.

```
        7    9  9  10
        8  km  1  0  0  0   m
 −      4  km     2  3  1   m
 ──────────────────────────
        3  km     7  6  9   m
```

It is 3 km 769 m *from her work to her house.*

   Lesson 1:   Express metric length measurements in terms of a smaller unit; model and solve addition and subtraction word problems involving metric length.

EUREKA MATH

G4-M2-Lesson 2

1. Complete the conversion table.

Mass	
kg	**g**
3	3,000
5	5,000
7	7,000

> I know that 1 kilogram equals 1,000 grams.

2. Convert the measurements.

   a. 4 kg 650 g   = __4,650__ g

   b. __51__ kg __45__ g = 51,045 g

> In 51,945, there are 51 thousands 945 ones. 1 thousand grams equals 1 kilogram, so 51 thousand grams 945 grams equals 51 kilograms 945 grams.

3. Solve.

   a. 7 kg − 860 g

> I make like units. 7 kilograms is equal to 7,000 grams.

$$7 \text{ kg} = 7,000 \text{ g}$$

Sample Student A Response:

```
        9
    6  10  10
   7,  0/  0/  0  g
 −      8   6  0  g
 ─────────────────
   6,   1   4  0  g
```

> I subtract grams from grams.

Sample Student B Response:

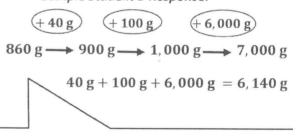

$$40 \text{ g} + 100 \text{ g} + 6,000 \text{ g} = 6,140 \text{ g}$$

> Just like in Lesson 1, I add up using the arrow way.

   b. Express the answer in the smaller unit: 23 kg 625 g + 526 g.

Sample Student A Response:

```
    2  3  kg    6  2  5  g
 +             5  2  6  g
 ─────────────────────────
               1
    2  3  kg  1  1  5  1  g
```

> I add and then convert the answer to grams.

$$23 \text{ kg} = 23,000 \text{ g}$$

$$23,000 \text{ g} + 1,151 \text{ g} = 24,151 \text{ g}$$

Sample Student B Response:

```
    2  3,  6  2  5  g
 +          5  2  6  g
 ─────────────────────
         1     1
    2  4,  1  5  1  g
```

> I rename 23 kg 625 grams as grams before adding.

Lesson 2: Express metric mass measurements in terms of a smaller unit; model and solve addition and subtraction word problems involving metric mass.

3

©2015 Great Minds. eureka-math.org
G4-M1-HWH-1.3.0-07.2015

c. Express the answer in mixed units: 18 kg 604 g – 3,461 g.

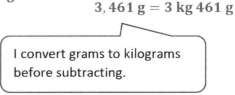

$3,461 \text{ g} = 3 \text{ kg } 461 \text{ g}$

```
              5   10
    1   8  kg  6̸   0̸   4  g
  –     3  kg  4   6   1  g
  ─────────────────────────
    1   5  kg  1   4   3  g
```

I convert grams to kilograms before subtracting.

Use a tape diagram to model each problem. Solve using a simplifying strategy or an algorithm, and write your answer as a statement.

4. One crate of watermelon weighs 18 kilograms 685 grams. Another crate of watermelon weighs 17 kilograms 435 grams. What is their combined weight?

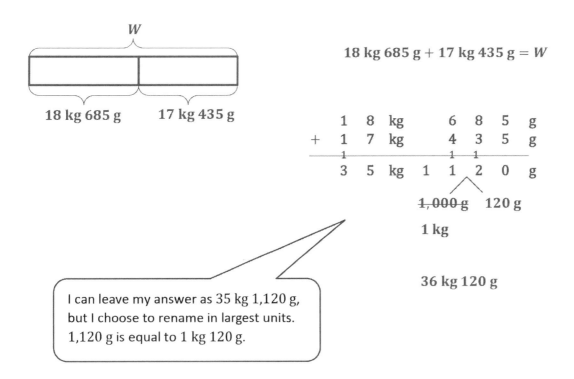

$18 \text{ kg } 685 \text{ g} + 17 \text{ kg } 435 \text{ g} = W$

```
        1  8  kg      6  8  5  g
    +   1  7  kg      4  3  5  g
        ─1─          ─1──1─
        3  5  kg   1  1  2  0  g
```

1,000 g   120 g

1 kg

36 kg 120 g

I can leave my answer as 35 kg 1,120 g, but I choose to rename in largest units. 1,120 g is equal to 1 kg 120 g.

The combined weight of the crates of watermelon is 36 kg 120 g.

Lesson 2: Express metric mass measurements in terms of a smaller unit; model and solve addition and subtraction word problems involving metric mass.

EUREKA MATH

G4-M2-Lesson 3

1. Complete the conversion table.

Liquid Capacity	
L	mL
6	6,000
18	18,000
32	32,000

There are 1,000 milliliters in 1 liter. The rule for converting is the same from Lesson 1 and 2.

2. Convert the measurements.

   a.   26 L 38 mL   =   __26,038__ mL

   b.   427,009 mL   =   __427__ L __9__ mL

I remember doing these conversions in Lessons 1 and 2, just with different units.

3. Solve.

   a.   Express the answer in the smaller unit:

   32 L 420 mL + 685 mL

```
      3  2,  4  2  0  mL
   +         6  8  5  mL
   ─────────1──1──────────
      3  3,  1  0  5  mL
```

Before adding, I rename 32 L 420 mL as milliliters since the answer is to be in the smaller unit.

   b.   Express the answer in mixed units:

   62 L 608 mL − 35 L 739 mL

```
                    15
       5  11        0  5  9  18
       6   1        1  6  0  8
      6  2  L      6  0  8  mL
   −  3  5  L      7  3  9  mL
   ─────────      ──────────────
      2  6  L      8  6  9  mL
```

I can subtract mixed units as given, or I can rename the units to the smallest unit, subtract, and then rename as mixed units.

EUREKA MATH™

Lesson 3: Express metric capacity measurements in terms of a smaller unit; model and solve addition and subtraction word problems involving metric capacity.

©2015 Great Minds. eureka-math.org
G4-M1-HWH-1.3.0-07.2015

5

G4-M2-Lesson 4

1. Complete the table.

Smaller Unit	Larger Unit	How Many Times as Large as?
ten	thousand	100

> I ask myself, "One thousand is 100 times as large as what unit?" I know 1 thousand is 100 tens (1 × 100 tens). So, my smaller unit is ten.

2. Fill in the unknown unit in word form.

125 is 1 _____*hundred*_____ 25 ones.   125 cm is 1 _____*meter*_____ 25 cm.

> I ask myself, "125 ones is the same as 1 of what larger unit and 25 ones?"

> The units are centimeters. I can make a larger unit. 100 centimeters equals 1 meter. So, 1 meter 25 cm is the same as 125 cm.

3. Write the unknown number.

____**142,728**____ is 142 thousands 728 ones.   ____**142,728**____ mL is 142 L 728 mL.

> I can decompose 142 thousands 728 into smaller units. 142 thousands is the same as 142,000 ones. So, 142 thousands 728 ones is 142,728.

> I know 1 liter equals 1,000 milliliters. So, 142 liters equals 142,000 milliliters, and 142 liters 728 milliliters equals 142,728 milliliters.

4. Fill in each with >, <, or =.

740,259 mL   (>)   74 L 249 mL

> 74 L 249 mL is the same as 74,249 mL. 74 ten thousands is greater than 7 ten thousands.

Lesson 4:   Know and relate metric units to place value units in order to express
                  measurements in different units.

EUREKA
MATH

5. Mikal's backpack weighs 4,289 grams. Mikal weighs 17 kilograms 989 grams more than his backpack. How much do Mikal and his backpack weigh in all?

$1 \text{ kg} = 1,000 \text{ g}$

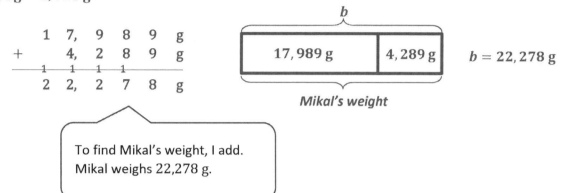

```
  1 7, 9 8 9  g
+    4, 2 8 9  g
  1  1 1 1
  2 2, 2 7 8  g
```

To find Mikal's weight, I add. Mikal weighs 22,278 g.

17,989 g | 4,289 g $b = 22,278 \text{ g}$

Mikal's weight

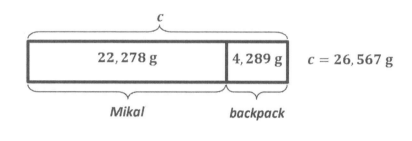

```
  2 2, 2 7 8  g
+    4, 2 8 9  g
     1 1
  2 6, 5 6 7  g
```

I add to find the total weight.

22,278 g | 4,289 g $c = 26,567 \text{ g}$

Mikal   *backpack*

Altogether Mikal and his backpack weigh 26,567 g *or* 26 kg 567 g.

6. Place the following measurements on the number line:

   1 kg 282 g   2,089 g   2 kg 92 g   3,219 g   100 g

Each unit on the number line is 1,000 g. I label each tick mark.

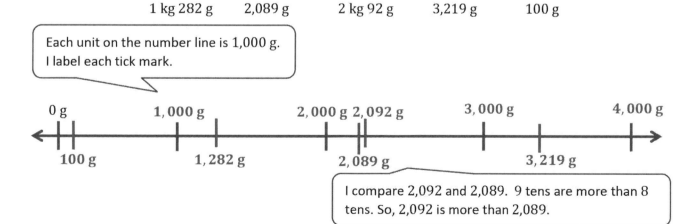

0 g   1,000 g   2,000 g 2,092 g   3,000 g   4,000 g

100 g   1,282 g   2,089 g   3,219 g

I compare 2,092 and 2,089. 9 tens are more than 8 tens. So, 2,092 is more than 2,089.

EUREKA MATH

Lesson 4: Know and relate metric units to place value units in order to express measurements in different units.

7

©2015 Great Minds. eureka-math.org
G4-M1-HWH-1.3.0-07.2015

G4-M2-Lesson 5

1. David weighs 46 kilograms 89 grams. Adam weighs 3,741 grams less than David. Joseph weighs 2,801 grams less than Adam. How much does Joseph weigh?

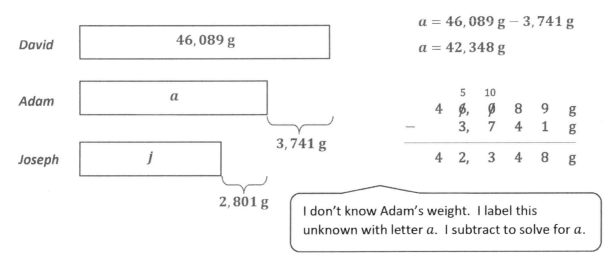

$$a = 46,089 \text{ g} - 3,741 \text{ g}$$
$$a = 42,348 \text{ g}$$

David | 46,089 g

Adam | a

Joseph | j

3,741 g

2,801 g

> I don't know Adam's weight. I label this unknown with letter a. I subtract to solve for a.

$$j = 42,348 \text{ g} - 2,801 \text{ g}$$
$$j = 39,547 \text{ g}$$

> Now that I know Adam's weight, I solve for j (Joseph's weight).

Joseph weighs 39,547 grams.

Lesson 5:   Use addition and subtraction to solve multi-step word problems involving length, mass, and capacity.

EUREKA MATH

2. Box A weighs 30 kilograms 490 grams. Box B weighs 6,790 grams less than Box A. Box C weighs 13 kilograms 757 grams more than Box B. What is the difference, in grams, between the weights of Box C and Box A?

Box A | 30, 490 g |

Box B | B | 6, 790 g |

Box C | | 13, 757 g |
        C

> I know Box B weighs 6,790 grams less than Box A. I label this part and subtract to solve for "B". Box B weighs 23,700 g.

$B = 30,490\text{ g} - 6,790\text{ g}$

$B = 23,700\text{ g}$

$$
\begin{array}{r}
\overset{2}{}\overset{9}{}\overset{14}{} \\
3\,0, \ 4 \ 9 \ 0 \ \text{g} \\
- \quad 6, \ 7 \ 9 \ 0 \ \text{g} \\
\hline
2 \ 3, \ 7 \ 0 \ 0 \ \text{g}
\end{array}
$$

> I know Box C weighs 13,757 grams more than Box B. If Box B weighs 23,700 grams, I can add to find "C". Box C weighs 37,457 g.

$$
\begin{array}{r}
2 \ 3, \ 7 \ 0 \ 0 \ \text{g} \\
+ \ 1 \ 3, \ 7 \ 5 \ 7 \ \text{g} \\
\hline
3 \ 7, \ 4 \ 5 \ 7 \ \text{g}
\end{array}
$$

D

Box A | 30, 490 g |

Box C | 37, 457 g |

> I know the weights of Boxes A and C. I can subtract to find the difference, D.

$D = 37,457\text{ g} - 30,490\text{ g}$

$D = 6,967\text{ g}$

$$
\begin{array}{r}
\overset{13}{} \\
\overset{6}{} \ \overset{7}{} \ \overset{15}{} \\
3 \ 7, \ 4 \ 5 \ 7 \ \text{g} \\
- \ 3 \ 0, \ 4 \ 9 \ 0 \ \text{g} \\
\hline
6, \ 9 \ 6 \ 7 \ \text{g}
\end{array}
$$

The difference between the weights of Box C and Box A is 6, 967 g.

Grade 4
Module 3

G4-M3-Lesson 1

1. Determine the perimeter and area of rectangles A and B.

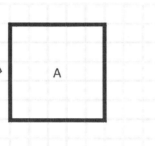

To find the area of rectangle A, I can skip count the square units inside: 5, 10, 15, 20, 25. Or I can multiply: $5 \times 5 = 25$.

I can't see the units inside rectangle B. So, I count the number of units for the side lengths and use the formula for area ($A = l \times w$).

  a. $A =$ ___**25 square units**___ $A =$ ___**28 square units**___

  b. $P =$ ___**20 units**___ $P =$ ___**22 units**___

I can use a formula for perimeter such as $P = 2 \times (l + w)$, $P = l + w + l + w$, or $P = 2l + 2w$.

2. Given the rectangle's area, find the unknown side length.

4 cm

I can think, "4 times what number equals 36?" Or, I can divide to find the unknown side length: $A \div l = w$.

b cm   36 square cm

$A = l \times w$
$36 = 4 \times b$
$b = 9$

$b =$ ___**9**___

The unknown side length of the rectangle is 9 centimeters.

Lesson 1:   Investigate and use the formulas for area and perimeter of rectangles.   1

3. The perimeter of this rectangle is 250 centimeters. Find the unknown side length of this rectangle.

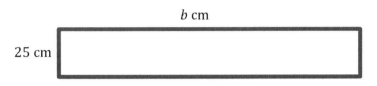

$$P = w + w + l + l$$
$$250 = 25 + 25 + l + l$$
$$250 = 50 + l + l$$

$$250 - 50 = 200$$

$$200 \div 2 = b$$
$$100 = b$$

I subtract to find the sum of the unknown sides.
I divide to find the unknown length, b cm.

The length of the rectangle is 100 cm.

4. The following rectangle has whole number side lengths. Given the area and perimeter, find the length and width.

$$A = 48 \text{ square cm}$$
$$P = 32 \text{ cm}$$

I list factor pairs for 48.

Dimensions of a
48 square cm Rectangle

$l = $ ___12 cm___

$w = $ ___4 cm___

Width	Length
1 cm	48 cm
2 cm	24 cm
3 cm	16 cm
4 cm	12 cm
6 cm	8 cm

I try the different possible factors as side lengths as I solve for a perimeter of 32 cm using the formula $P = 2L + 2W$.

$$P = (2 \times 8) + (2 \times 6)$$
$$P = 16 + 12$$
$$P = 28$$

$$P = (2 \times 12) + (2 \times 4)$$
$$P = 24 + 8$$
$$P = 32$$

No!

Yes! The factors 4 and 12 work!

EUREKA
MATH

G4-M3-Lesson 2

1. A rectangular pool is 2 feet wide. It is 4 times as long as it is wide.

   a. Label the diagram with the dimensions of the pool.

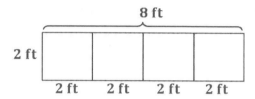

   b. Find the perimeter of the pool.

   $P = 2 \times (l + w)$
   $P = 2 \times (8 + 2)$
   $P = 2 \times 10$
   $P = 20$

   > I choose one of the 3 formulas I learned in Lesson 1 to solve for perimeter.

   The perimeter of the pool is 20 ft.

2. The area of Brette's bedroom rug is 6 square feet. The longer side measures 3 feet. Her living room rug is twice as long and twice as wide as the bedroom rug.

   a. Draw and label a diagram of Brette's bedroom rug. What is its perimeter?

   $A = l \times w$
   $6 = 3 \times w$

   $b = 6 \div 3$ > I divide to find the width.
   $b = 2$

   $P = 2l + 2w$

   $P = (2 \times 3) + (2 \times 2)$

   $P = 6 + 4$

   $P = 10$

   The perimeter of Brette's bedroom rug is 10 ft.

b.   Draw and label a diagram of Brette's living room rug. What is its perimeter?

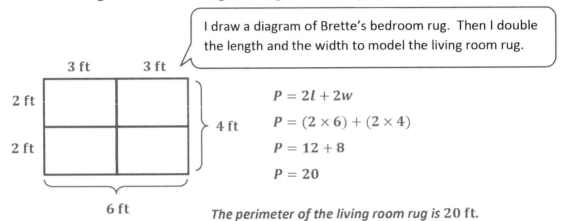

> I draw a diagram of Brette's bedroom rug. Then I double the length and the width to model the living room rug.

$$P = 2l + 2w$$
$$P = (2 \times 6) + (2 \times 4)$$
$$P = 12 + 8$$
$$P = 20$$

The perimeter of the living room rug is 20 *ft.*

c.   What is the relationship between the two perimeters?

Sample Answer: The perimeter of the bedroom rug is 10 *ft. The perimeter of the living room rug is* 20 *ft. The living room rug is double the perimeter of the bedroom rug. I know because* $2 \times 10 = 20$.

> I explain a pattern I notice. I verify my thinking with an equation.

d.   Find the area of the living room rug using the formula $A = l \times w$.

$A = l \times w$ *The area of the living room rug is* 24 *square feet.*

$A = 6 \times 4$

$A = 24$

e.   The living room rug has an area that is how many times that of the bedroom rug?

Sample Answer: The area of the bedroom rug is 6 *square feet. The area of the living room rug is* 24 *square feet. 4 times 6 is 24. The area of the living room rug is 4 times the area of the bedroom rug.*

f.   Compare how the perimeter changed with how the area changed between the two rugs. Explain what you notice using words, pictures, or numbers.

Sample Answer: The perimeter of the living room rug is 2 *times the perimeter of the bedroom rug. But, the area of the living room rug is* 4 *times the area of the bedroom rug! I notice that when we double each of the side lengths, the perimeter doubles, and the area quadruples.*

Lesson 2:   Solve multiplicative comparison word problems by applying the area and perimeter formulas.

EUREKA MATH™

G4-M3-Lesson 3

Solve the following problems. Use pictures, numbers, or words to show your work.

1. A calendar is 2 times as long and 3 times as wide as a business card. The business card is 2 inches long and 1 inch wide. What is the perimeter of the calendar?

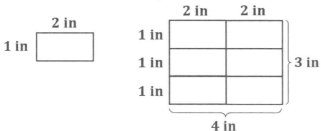

$P = 2 \times (l + w)$

$P = 2 \times (4 \text{ in} + 3 \text{ in})$

$P = 2 \times 7 \text{ in}$

$P = 14 \text{ in}$

The perimeter of the calendar is 14 inches.

I draw a diagram with a width 3 times that of the card (3 in).
I label the length to equal twice the width of the card (4 in).

2. Rectangle A has an area of 64 square centimeters. Rectangle A is 8 times as many square centimeters as rectangle B. If rectangle B is 4 centimeters wide, what is the length of rectangle B?

There are so many ways to solve!

64 square cm

Rectangle A

1 unit = B square cm

8 units = 64 square cm

$64 \div 8 = B$

$B = 8$

The area of rectangle B is 8 square centimeters.

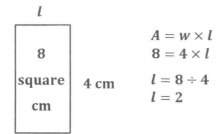

$A = w \times l$

$8 = 4 \times l$

$l = 8 \div 4$

$l = 2$

Rectangle B   *The length of rectangle B is 2 cm.*

Lesson 3: Demonstrate understanding of area and perimeter formulas by solving multi-step real-world problems.

©2015 Great Minds. eureka-math.org
G4-M1-HWH-1.3.0-07.2015

G4-M3-Lesson 4

1. Fill in the blanks in the following equations.

   a. __100__ × 7 = 700   b. 4 × __1,000__ = 4,000   c. __50__ = 10 × 5

   > I ask myself, "How many sevens are equal to 700?"

   > I use unit form to solve. If I name the units, multiplying large numbers is easy! I know 4 ÷ 4 = 1, so 4 thousands ÷ 4 is 1 thousand.

Draw place value disks and arrows to represent each product.

2. 15 × 100 = __1,500__

    15 × 10 × 10 = __1,500__

    (1 ten 5 ones) × 100 = __1 thousand 5 hundreds__

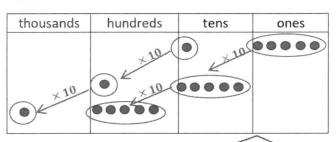

thousands	hundreds	tens	ones

> Fifteen is 1 ten 5 ones. I draw an arrow to show times 10 for the 1 ten and also for the 5 ones. I multiply by 10 again and I have 1 thousand 5 hundreds.

> If I shift a digit one place to the left on the chart, that digit becomes 10 times as much as its value to the right.

Decompose each multiple of 10, 100, or 1,000 before multiplying.

3. 2 × 300 = 2 × __3__ × __100__
    = __6__ × __100__
    = __600__

4. 6 × 7,000 = __6__ × __7__ × __1,000__
    = __42__ × __1,000__
    = __42,000__

> I can decompose 300 to make an easy fact to solve! I know 2 × 3 hundreds = 6 hundreds.

EUREKA
MATH

G4-M3-Lesson 5

1. $2 \times 4,000 =$ ___8,000___

    ___2___ times ___4 thousands___ is ___8 thousands___ .

thousands	hundreds	tens	ones
●●●● ●●●●			

I draw 2 groups of 4 thousands and circle each group. I see a pattern! 2 groups of 4 units is 8 units.

$$
\begin{array}{r}
4,\;0\;\;0\;\;0 \\
\times \qquad\qquad 2 \\
\hline
8,\;0\;\;0\;\;0
\end{array}
$$

2×4 thousands $= 8$ thousands

Writing the equation in unit form helps me when one of the factors is a multiple of 10.

2. Find the product.

a. $4 \times 70 = 280$	b. $4 \times 60 = 240$	c. $4 \times 500 = 2,000$	d. $6,000 \times 5 = 30,000$
4×7 tens $= 28$ tens	4×6 tens $= 24$ tens	4×5 hundreds $= 20$ hundreds	6 thousands $\times 5$ $= 30$ thousands

3. At the school cafeteria, each student who orders lunch gets 7 chicken nuggets. The cafeteria staff prepares enough for 400 kids. How many chicken nuggets does the cafeteria staff prepare altogether?

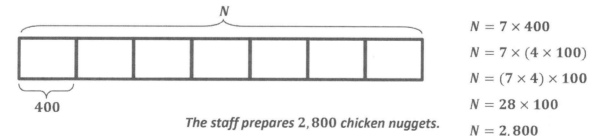

$N = 7 \times 400$

$N = 7 \times (4 \times 100)$

$N = (7 \times 4) \times 100$

$N = 28 \times 100$

The staff prepares 2,800 chicken nuggets.

$N = 2,800$

I can decompose 400 into 4×100 to unveil an easy fact (7×4). Or I can use unit form to solve. 7 times 4 hundreds is 28 hundreds.

G4-M3-Lesson 6

Represent the following problem by drawing disks in the place value chart.

1. To solve 30×40, think:

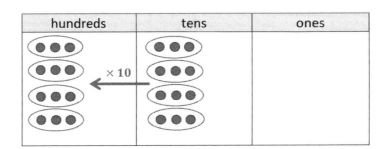

   $(3 \text{ tens} \times 4) \times 10 = \underline{1,200}$

   $30 \times (4 \times 10) = \underline{1,200}$

   $30 \times 40 = \underline{1,200}$

   I draw 4 groups of 3 tens multiplied by 10.

2. Draw an area model to represent 30×40.

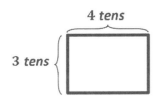

   4 tens

   3 tens

   3 tens $\times$ 12 tens= __hundreds__

   When I multiply tens by tens, I get hundreds.

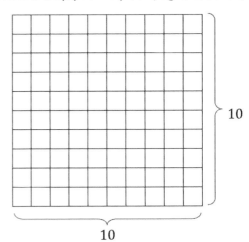

   10

   10

Rewrite each equation in unit form and solve.

3. $80 \times 60 = \underline{4,800}$

   $\underline{8}$ __tens__ $\times$ $\underline{6}$ __tens__ $= \underline{48}$ hundreds

4. One carton contains 70 eggs. If there are 70 cartons in a crate, how many eggs are in one crate?

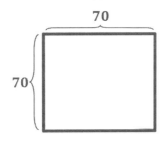

   70

   70

   7 tens $\times$ 7 tens $= 49$ hundreds

   $70 \times 70 = 4,900$

   There are $4,900$ eggs in one crate.

Lesson 6:   Multiply two-digit multiples of 10 by two-digit multiples of 10 with the area model.

EUREKA
MATH

G4-M3-Lesson 7

1. Represent the following expression with disks, regrouping as necessary. To the right, record the partial products vertically.

4×35

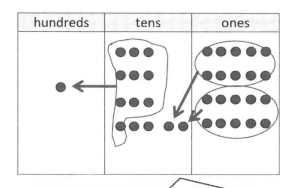

$$
\begin{array}{r}
3\ 5 \\
\times \qquad 4 \\
\hline
2\ 0 \quad \rightarrow 4 \times 5\ \textit{ones} \\
+\ 1\ 2\ 0 \quad \rightarrow 4 \times 3\ \textit{tens} \\
\hline
1\ 4\ 0 \\
\end{array}
$$

I draw 4 groups of 3 tens 5 ones.

4 times 5 ones equals 20 ones.

I compose 20 ones to make 2 tens.

4 times 3 tens equals 12 tens.

I compose 10 tens to make 1 hundred.

After multiplying the ones, I record the product. I multiply the tens and record the product. I add these two partial products. My sum is the product of 35×4.

2. Jillian says she found a shortcut for doing multiplication problems. When she multiplies 3×45, she says, "3×5 is 15 ones, or 1 ten and 5 ones. Then, there's just 4 tens left in 45, so add it up, and you get 5 tens and 5 ones." Do you think Jillian's shortcut works? Explain your thinking in words, and justify your response using a model or partial products.

Sample answer:

Jillian multiplied the ones. She found the first partial product. But she didn't multiply the tens. She forgot to multiply 4 tens by 3. So, Jillian didn't get the right second partial product. So, her final product isn't correct. The product of 3×45 is 135.

$$
\begin{array}{r}
4\ 5 \\
\times \qquad 3 \\
\hline
1\ 5 \quad \rightarrow 3 \times 5\ \textit{ones} \\
+\ 1\ 2\ 0 \quad \rightarrow 3 \times 4\ \textit{tens} \\
\hline
1\ 3\ 5 \\
\end{array}
$$

G4-M3-Lesson 8

Represent the following with disks, using either method shown in class, regrouping as necessary. Below the place value chart, record the partial product vertically.

1. 5×731

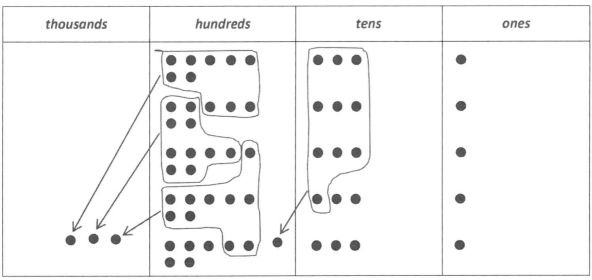

thousands	hundreds	tens	ones

5×7 *hundreds* + 5×3 *tens* + 5×1 *one*

3 *thousands* + 6 *hundreds* + 5 *tens* + 5 *ones* $= 3,655$

> When there are 10 units in any place, I compose a larger unit.

$$
\begin{array}{r}
7 \; 3 \; 1 \\
\times \qquad 5 \\
\hline
5 \quad \rightarrow 5 \times 1 \text{ one}\\
1 \; 5 \; 0 \quad \rightarrow 5 \times 3 \text{ tens}\\
+ \; 3, \; 5 \; 0 \; 0 \quad \rightarrow 5 \times 7 \text{ hundreds}\\
\hline
3, \; 6 \; 5 \; 5
\end{array}
$$

> The partial products mirror the disks on the place value chart. I draw and record the total value of each unit.

Lesson 8:   Extend the use of place value disks to represent three- and four-digit by one-digit multiplication.

©2015 Great Minds. eureka-math.org
G4-M1-HWH-1.3.0-07.2015

2. Janice rides her bike around the block. The block is rectangular with a width of 172 m and a length of 230 m.

   a. Determine how many meters Janice rides if she goes around the block one time.

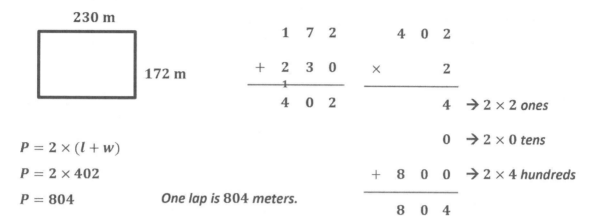

$$P = 2 \times (l + w)$$
$$P = 2 \times 402$$
$$P = 804$$ *One lap is 804 meters.*

   b. Determine how many meters Janice rides if she goes around the block three times.

```
        8  0  4
   ×          3
   _____
           1  2   → 3 × 4 ones
              0   → 3 × 0 tens
 +  2,  4  0  0   → 3 × 8 hundreds
   _____
    2,  4  1  2
```

Janice rides 2,412 meters.

EUREKA MATH   **Lesson 8:**   Extend the use of place value disks to represent three- and four-digit by one-digit multiplication.   **11**

©2015 Great Minds. eureka-math.org
G4-M1-HWH-1.3.0-07.2015

G4-M3-Lesson 9

1. Solve using each method.

No matter which method I choose, I get the same product.

When using the standard algorithm, I record the product all on one line.

Partial Products	Standard Algorithm
2 1 5 × 4	2 1 5 × 4
2 0 4 0 + 8 0 0	8 6 0
8 6 0	

I envision my work with disks on the place value chart when I use the partial products method. I record each partial product on a separate line.

4 times 5 ones equals 20 ones or 2 tens 0 ones. I record 2 tens on the line in the tens place and 0 ones in the ones place.

2. Solve using the standard algorithm.

a.
```
    2 0 5
  ×     9
  ---------
  1, 8 4 5
```

b.
```
    4 9 1
  ×     7
  ---------
  3, 4 3 7
```

7 times 4 hundreds is 28 hundreds. I add 6 hundreds and record 34 hundreds. I cross out the 6 hundreds after I add them.

When using the standard algorithm, I multiply the ones first.

3. One airline ticket costs $249. How much will 4 tickets cost?

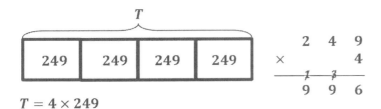

```
    2 4 9
  ×     4
  ---------
    9 9 6
```

I record 36 ones as 3 tens 6 ones. I write the 3 first and then the 6. It's easy to see 36 since the 3 is written on the line.

$T = 4 \times 249$

$T = 996$

Four tickets will cost $996.

Lesson 9: Multiply three- and four-digit numbers by one-digit numbers applying the standard algorithm.

EUREKA MATH

©2015 Great Minds. eureka-math.org
G4-M1-HWH-1.3.0-07.2015

G4-M3-Lesson 10

1. Solve using the standard algorithm.

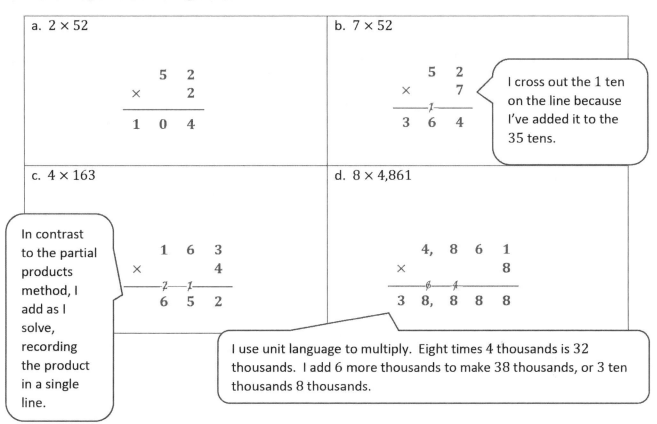

a. 2×52

$$
\begin{array}{r}
5\ 2 \\
\times\ \ \ \ 2 \\
\hline
1\ 0\ 4
\end{array}
$$

b. 7×52

$$
\begin{array}{r}
5\ 2 \\
\times\ \ \ \ 7 \\
\hline
3\ 6\ 4
\end{array}
$$

> I cross out the 1 ten on the line because I've added it to the 35 tens.

c. 4×163

$$
\begin{array}{r}
1\ 6\ 3 \\
\times\ \ \ \ \ \ 4 \\
\hline
6\ 5\ 2
\end{array}
$$

> In contrast to the partial products method, I add as I solve, recording the product in a single line.

d. $8 \times 4{,}861$

$$
\begin{array}{r}
4{,}\ 8\ 6\ 1 \\
\times\ \ \ \ \ \ \ \ \ \ 8 \\
\hline
3\ 8{,}\ 8\ 8\ 8
\end{array}
$$

> I use unit language to multiply. Eight times 4 thousands is 32 thousands. I add 6 more thousands to make 38 thousands, or 3 ten thousands 8 thousands.

2. Mimi ran 2 miles. Raj ran 3 times as far. There are 5,280 feet in a mile. How many feet did Raj run?

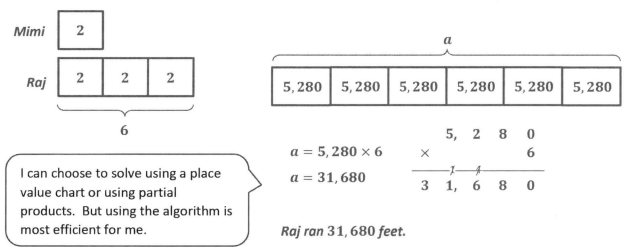

Mimi | 2

Raj | 2 | 2 | 2   6

| a |
| 5,280 | 5,280 | 5,280 | 5,280 | 5,280 | 5,280 |

> I can choose to solve using a place value chart or using partial products. But using the algorithm is most efficient for me.

$a = 5{,}280 \times 6$

$a = 31{,}680$

$$
\begin{array}{r}
5{,}\ 2\ 8\ 0 \\
\times\ \ \ \ \ \ \ \ \ \ 6 \\
\hline
3\ 1{,}\ 6\ 8\ 0
\end{array}
$$

Raj ran $31{,}680$ *feet.*

EUREKA MATH   **Lesson 10:**   Multiply three- and four-digit numbers by one-digit numbers applying the standard algorithm.   13

©2015 Great Minds. eureka-math.org
G4-M1-HWH-1.3.0-07.2015

G4-M3-Lesson 11

1. Solve the following expression using the standard algorithm, the partial products method, and the area model.

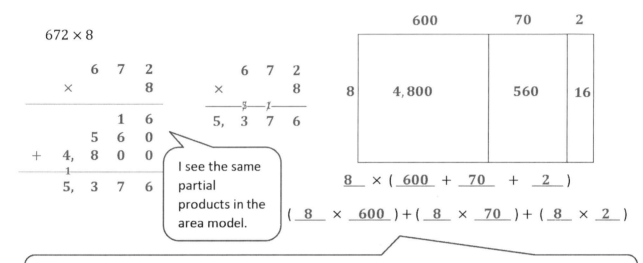

672×8

$$\begin{array}{r} 6\ 7\ 2 \\ \times\ \ \ \ \ 8 \\ \hline 1\ 6 \\ 5\ 6\ 0 \\ +\ 4,8\ 0\ 0 \\ \hline 5,3\ 7\ 6 \end{array}$$

$$\begin{array}{r} 6\ 7\ 2 \\ \times\ \ \ \ \ 8 \\ \hline 5,\ 3\ 7\ 6 \end{array}$$

I see the same partial products in the area model.

	600	70	2
8	4,800	560	16

$\underline{\ 8\ } \times (\ \underline{600}\ +\ \underline{70}\ +\ \underline{2}\ )$

$(\ \underline{8}\ \times\ \underline{600}\ ) + (\ \underline{8}\ \times\ \underline{70}\ ) + (\ \underline{8}\ \times\ \underline{2}\ )$

I multiply unit by unit when solving using partial products, the algorithm, or the area model. All along I have been using the distributive property! Now I can write it out as an expression to match.

2. Solve using the standard algorithm, the area model, the distributive property, or the partial products method.

Each year, Mr. Hill gives $5,725 to charity, and Mrs. Hill gives $752. After 5 years, how much has the couple given to charity?

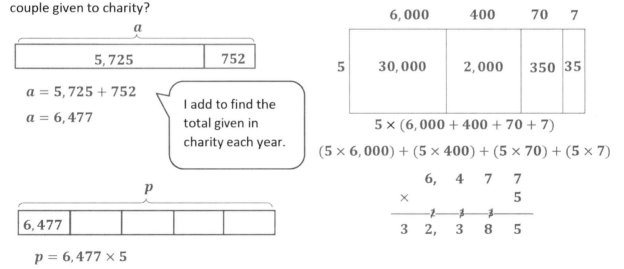

a	
5,725	752

$a = 5,725 + 752$

$a = 6,477$

I add to find the total given in charity each year.

	6,000	400	70	7
5	30,000	2,000	350	35

$5 \times (6,000 + 400 + 70 + 7)$

$(5 \times 6,000) + (5 \times 400) + (5 \times 70) + (5 \times 7)$

p				
6,477				

$$\begin{array}{r} 6,\ 4\ 7\ 7 \\ \times\ \ \ \ \ \ \ \ 5 \\ \hline 3\ 2,\ 3\ 8\ 5 \end{array}$$

$p = 6,477 \times 5$

$p = 32,385$

After 5 years, Mr. and Mrs. Hill have given $32,385 to charity.

Lesson 11: Connect the area model and the partial products method to the standard algorithm.

©2015 Great Minds. eureka-math.org
G4-M1-HWH-1.3.0-07.2015

G4-M3-Lesson 12

Use the RDW process to solve the following problem.

1. The table shows the cost of bake sale goods. Milan's mom buys 1 brownie, 1 cookie, and 1 slice of cake for each of her 8 children. How much does she spend?

Baked Good	Cost
brownie	59¢
slice of cake	45¢
cookie	27¢

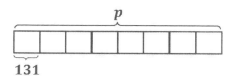

```
    5  9
    4  5
 +  2  7
 ───2───
    1  3  1
```

I add and then multiply to solve.

$p = 131 \times 8$

$p = 1,048$

```
       1  3  1
    ×        8
    ───7──────
    1, 0  4  8
```

Milan's mom spends 1,048¢.

2.

a. Write an equation that could be used to find the value of c in the tape diagram.

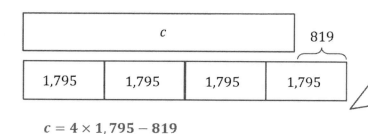

I thought of two other equations:

$c + 819 = 4 \times 1,795$

or

$c = (3 \times 1,795) + (1,795 - 819)$.

$c = 4 \times 1,795 - 819$

b. Write your own word problem to correspond to the tape diagram, and then solve.

Every month, Katrina earns $1,795. Kelly earns 4 times as much as Katrina earns. Mary earns $819 less than Kelly. How much does Mary earn each month?

$M = (4 \times 1,795) - 819$

$M = 7,180 - 819$

$M = 6,361$

```
    1, 7  9  5
  ×        4
  ──────────
       2  0
    3  6  0
 2, 8  0  0
+4, 0  0  0
 ──1───────
 7, 1  8  0
```

```
    6  11  7  10
 7, 1̶  8̶  0̶
 -  8  1  9
 ──────────
 6, 3  6  1
```

I use the partial products method to make sure I record the products of each unit.

Mary earns $6,361 each month.

G4-M3-Lesson 13

Solve using the RDW process.

1. A banana costs 58¢. A pomegranate costs 3 times as much. What is the total cost of a pomegranate and 5 bananas?

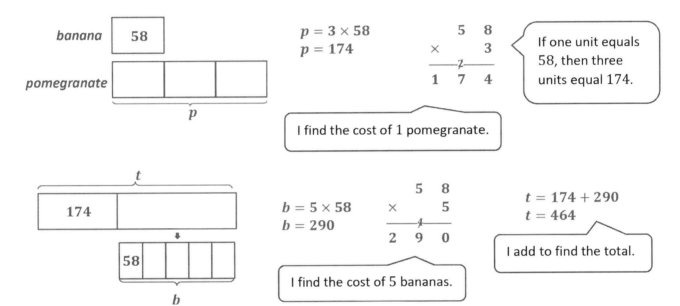

The total cost of a pomegranate and 5 bananas is 464¢.

2. Mr. Turner gave his 2 daughters $197 each. He gave his mother $325. He gave his wife money as well. If Mr. Turner gave a total of $3,000, how much did he give to his wife?

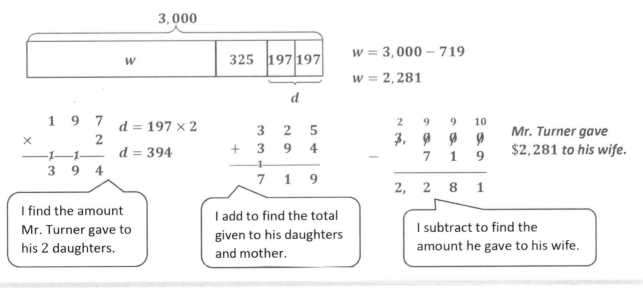

Lesson 13:   Use multiplication, addition, or subtraction to solve multi-step word problems.

EUREKA MATH

G4-M3-Lesson 14

Use the RDW process to solve the following problems.

1. Marco has 19 tortillas. If he uses 2 tortillas for each quesadilla, what is the greatest number of quesadillas he can make? Will he have any extra tortillas? How many?

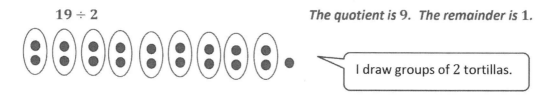

$19 \div 2$ *The quotient is 9. The remainder is 1.*

I draw groups of 2 tortillas.

He can make up to 9 quesadillas. He will have 1 extra tortilla.

2. Coach Adam puts 31 players into teams of 8. How many teams does he make? If he makes a smaller team with the remaining players, how many players are on that team?

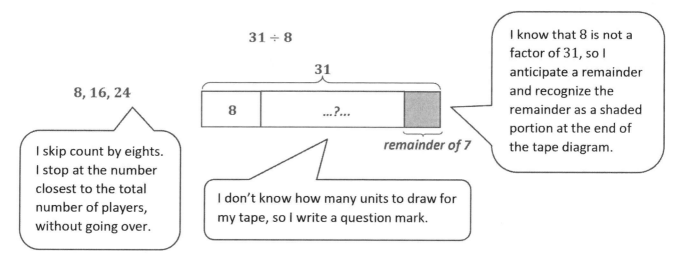

$31 \div 8$

I know that 8 is not a factor of 31, so I anticipate a remainder and recognize the remainder as a shaded portion at the end of the tape diagram.

8, 16, 24

I skip count by eights. I stop at the number closest to the total number of players, without going over.

I don't know how many units to draw for my tape, so I write a question mark.

remainder of 7

Coach Adam makes 3 teams. The smaller team has 7 players.

G4-M3-Lesson 15

Show division using an array.	Show division using an area model.

1. $21 \div 4$

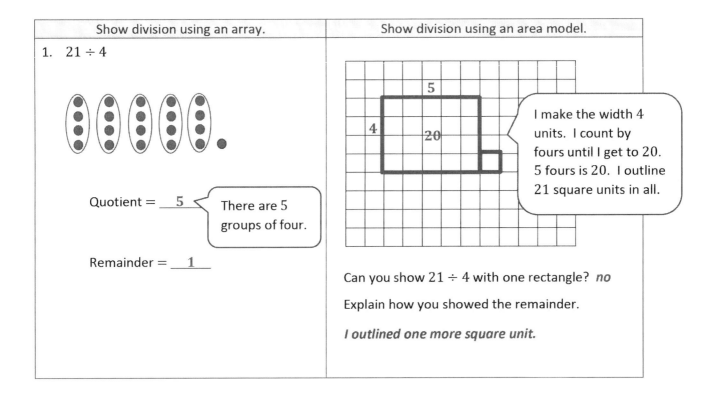

Quotient = **5**

There are 5 groups of four.

Remainder = **1**

I make the width 4 units. I count by fours until I get to 20. 5 fours is 20. I outline 21 square units in all.

Can you show $21 \div 4$ with one rectangle? *no*

Explain how you showed the remainder.

I outlined one more square unit.

Solve using an array and area model.

2. $53 \div 7$

I can draw quickly without grid paper.

a. Array

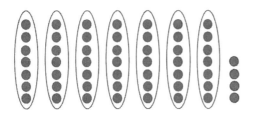

Quotient = 7   Remainder = 4

The area model may be faster to draw, but no matter which model I use, I get the same answer!

b. Area Model

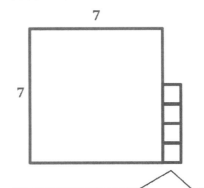

I represent the remainder with 4 more square units.

Lesson 15:   Understand and solve division problems with a remainder using the array and area models.

EUREKA MATH

G4-M3-Lesson 16

Show the division using disks. Relate your work on the place value chart to long division. Check your quotient and remainder by using multiplication and addition.

1. $9 \div 2$

> To model, the divisor represents the number of equal groups. The quotient represents the size of the groups.

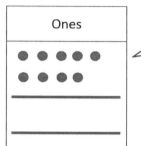

> I represent 9 ones, the whole, using place value disks.

> I make space on the chart to distribute the disks into 2 equal groups.

> 9 ones distributed evenly into 2 equal groups is 4 ones in each group. I cross them off as I distribute.

> 1 one remains because it cannot be distributed evenly into 2. I circle it to show it is a remainder.

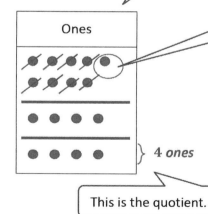

} 4 ones

> This is the quotient.

$$
\begin{array}{r}
4 \quad R1 \\
2\ \overline{)\ 9} \\
-\ 8 \\
\hline
1
\end{array}
$$

quotient = ___4___

remainder = ___1___

Check your work.

$$
\begin{array}{r}
4 \\
\times\ 2 \\
\hline
8
\end{array}
\qquad
\begin{array}{r}
8 \\
+\ 1 \\
\hline
9
\end{array}
$$

> I check my division by multiplying the quotient times the divisor. I add the remainder. The sum is the whole.

EUREKA
MATH™

Lesson 16:   Understand and solve two-digit dividend division problems with a remainder in the ones place by using place value disks.

19

©2015 Great Minds. eureka-math.org
G4-M1-HWH-1.3.0-07.2015

2. $87 \div 4$

I represent the whole as 8 tens and 7 ones. I partition the chart into 4 equal groups below.

Tens	Ones

$8 \div 4 = 2$

8 tens distributed evenly among 4 groups is 2 tens.

$$\begin{array}{r} 2 \\ 4\,\overline{\smash{\big)}\,8\ 7} \\ -\ 8 \\ \hline 0\ 7 \end{array}$$

$2 \times 4 = 8$

2 tens in each of the 4 groups is 8 tens.

$8 - 8 = 0$

We started with 8 tens and distributed 8 tens evenly. Zero tens and 7 ones remain in the whole.

$7 \div 4 = 1$

7 ones distributed evenly among 4 groups is 1 one.

Tens	Ones
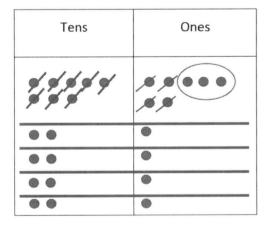	

} *2 tens 1 one*

$$\begin{array}{r} 2\ \ 1\ \ R3 \\ 4\,\overline{\smash{\big)}\,8\ 7} \\ -\ 8 \\ \hline 0\ 7 \\ -\ 4 \\ \hline 3 \end{array}$$

$4 \times 1 = 4$

1 one in each of the 4 groups is 4 ones. Only 4 of the 7 ones were evenly distributed.

$7 - 4 = 3$

We started with 7 ones and distributed 4 ones evenly. 3 ones remain in the whole.

I record the remainder next to the quotient.

quotient = __21__

remainder = __3__

Check your work

$$\begin{array}{r} 2\ \ 1 \\ \times\ \ \ \ 4 \\ \hline 8\ \ 4 \end{array} \qquad \begin{array}{r} 8\ \ 4 \\ +\ \ \ 3 \\ \hline 8\ \ 7 \end{array}$$

EUREKA
MATH

G4-M3-Lesson 17

Show the division using disks. Relate your model to long division. Check your quotient by using multiplication and addition.

1. 5 ÷ 4

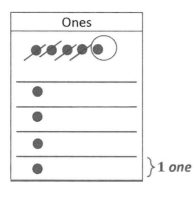

Ones

```
   1   R1
4 │ 5
 −   4
 ─────
     1
```

quotient = __1__

remainder = __1__

} **1 one**

Check your work.

```
    4          4
×   1      +   1
─────      ─────
    4          5
```

> Just like Lesson 16, I model the whole and partition the chart into 4 parts to represent the divisor.

2. 53 ÷ 4

> After distributing 4 tens, 1 ten remains. I change 1 ten for 10 ones.

> Now, I have 13 ones. I can distribute 12 ones evenly, but 1 one remains.

Tens	Ones

```
    1  3   R1
4 │ 5  3
 −  4
 ──────
    1  3
 −  1  2
 ──────
       1
```

} **1 ten 3 ones**

quotient = __13__

remainder = __1__

Check your work.

```
    1  3         5  2
×      4      +     1
──────        ──────
    5  2         5  3
```

Lesson 17:   Represent and solve division problems requiring decomposing a
remainder in the tens.

21

©2015 Great Minds. eureka-math.org
G4-M1-HWH-1.3.0-07.2015

G4-M3-Lesson 18

Solve using the standard algorithm. Check your quotient and remainder by using multiplication and addition.

1. $69 \div 3$

$$
\begin{array}{r}
2\ 3 \\
3\ \overline{|\ 6\ 9} \\
-\ 6 \\
\hline
0\ 9 \\
-\ \ \ 9 \\
\hline
0
\end{array}
$$

$$
\begin{array}{r}
2\ \ 3 \\
\times\ \ \ \ 3 \\
\hline
6\ \ 9
\end{array}
$$

> 69 divided by 3 is 23. And 23 times 3 is 69.

2. $57 \div 3$

> I notice the divisor is the same in Problems 1 and 2. But the whole 69 is greater than the whole of 57. When the divisor is the same, the larger the whole, the larger the quotient.

$$
\begin{array}{r}
1\ 9 \\
3\ \overline{|\ 5\ 7} \\
-\ 3 \\
\hline
2\ 7 \\
-\ 2\ 7 \\
\hline
0
\end{array}
$$

> I distribute 3 tens. 2 tens remain. After decomposing, 20 ones plus 7 ones is 27 ones.

$$
\begin{array}{r}
1\ \ 9 \\
\times\ \ \ \ 3 \\
\hline
5\ \ 7
\end{array}
$$

3. $94 \div 5$

$$
\begin{array}{r}
1\ 8\ R4 \\
5\ \overline{|\ 9\ 4} \\
-\ 5 \\
\hline
4\ 4 \\
-\ 4\ 0 \\
\hline
4
\end{array}
$$

$$
\begin{array}{r}
1\ \ 8 \\
\times\ \ \ \ 5 \\
\hline
9\ \ 0
\end{array}
\qquad
\begin{array}{r}
9\ \ 0 \\
+\ \ \ \ 4 \\
\hline
9\ \ 4
\end{array}
$$

> The quotient is 18 with a remainder of 4.

4. $97 \div 7$

> When the wholes are nearly the same, the larger the divisor, the smaller the quotient. That's because the whole is divided into more equal groups.

$$
\begin{array}{r}
1\ 3\ R6 \\
7\ \overline{|\ 9\ 7} \\
-\ 7 \\
\hline
2\ 7 \\
-\ 2\ 1 \\
\hline
6
\end{array}
$$

$$
\begin{array}{r}
1\ \ 3 \\
\times\ \ \ \ 7 \\
\hline
9\ \ 1
\end{array}
\qquad
\begin{array}{r}
9\ \ 1 \\
+\ \ \ \ 6 \\
\hline
9\ \ 7
\end{array}
$$

> I prove my division is correct by multiplying 13 by 7 and then adding 6 more.

EUREKA MATH

G4-M3-Lesson 19

1. Makhai says that $97 \div 3$ is 30 with a remainder of 7. He reasons this is correct
    because $(3 \times 30) + 7 = 97$. What mistake has Makhai made? Explain how he can
    correct his work.

    Makhai stopped dividing when he had 7 ones, but he can distribute them into 3
    more groups of 2. If he does so, he can make 3 groups of 32 instead of just 30.

    > There are not enough ones to
    > distribute into 3 groups. I record 1
    > one as the remainder.

    ```
          3 2  R1
        ┌──────
      3 │ 9 7
        − 9
        ──────
          0 7
          − 6
        ──────
            1
    ```

2. Four friends evenly share 52 dollars.

    a. They have 5 ten-dollar bills and 2 one-dollar bills. Draw a picture to show how the bills will be
        shared. Will they have to make change at any stage?

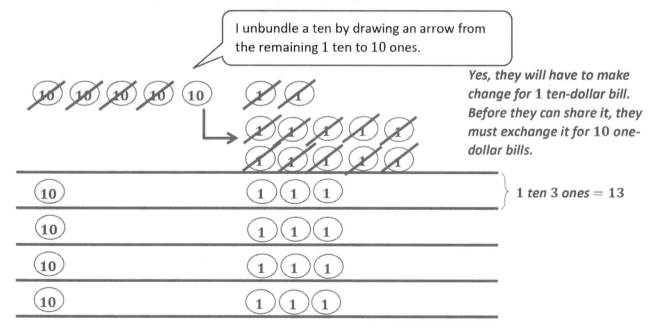

    > I unbundle a ten by drawing an arrow from
    > the remaining 1 ten to 10 ones.

    Yes, they will have to make
    change for 1 ten-dollar bill.
    Before they can share it, they
    must exchange it for 10 one-
    dollar bills.

    1 ten 3 ones = 13

    b. Explain how they share the money evenly.

        Each friend gets 1 ten-dollar bill and 3 one-dollar bills.

3. Imagine you are writing a magazine article describing how to solve the problem $43 \div 3$ to new fourth graders. Write a draft to explain how you can keep dividing after getting a remainder of 1 ten in the first step.

Sample answer: This is how you divide 43 by 3. Think of it like 4 tens 3 ones divided into 3 groups. First, you want to distribute the tens. You can distribute 3 tens. Each group will have 1 ten. There will be 1 ten left over. That's okay. You can keep dividing. Just change 1 ten for 10 ones. Now you have 13 ones altogether. You can distribute 12 ones evenly. 3 groups of 4 ones is 12 ones. 1 one is remaining. So, your quotient is 14 R1. And that's how you divide 43 by 3.

```
          1  4  R1
      ┌──────────
   3  │  4  3
      −  3
      ──────────
         1  3
      −  1  2
      ──────────
            1
```

Lesson 19:   Explain remainders by using place value understanding and models

EUREKA MATH

©2015 Great Minds. eureka-math.org
G4-M1-HWH-1.3.0-07.2015

G4-M3-Lesson 20

1. Paco solved a division problem by drawing an area model.

   a. Look at the area model. What division problem did Paco solve?

   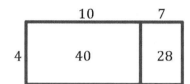

   $68 \div 4 = 17$

   I add the areas to find the whole. The width is the divisor. I add the two lengths to find the quotient.

   b. Show a number bond to represent Paco's area model. Start with the total, and then show how the total is split into two parts. Below the two parts, represent the total length using the distributive property, and then solve.

   Dividing smaller numbers is easier for me than solving $68 \div 4$. I can solve mentally because these are easy facts.

   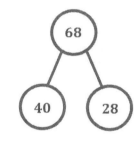

   In the number bond, I record the whole (68) split into two parts (40 and 28).

   $$(\underline{\ 40\ } \div \underline{\ 4\ }) + (\underline{\ 28\ } \div \underline{\ 4\ })$$

   $$= \underline{\ 10\ } + \underline{\ 7\ }$$

   $$= \underline{\ 17\ }$$

2. Solve $76 \div 4$ using an area model. Explain the connection of the distributive property to the area model using words, pictures, or numbers.

   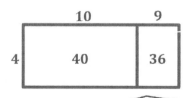

   $$(40 \div 4) + (36 \div 4)$$

   $$= 10 + 9$$

   $$= 19$$

   The area model is like a picture for the distributive model. Each rectangle represents a smaller division expression that we write in parentheses. The width of the rectangle is the divisor in each sentence. The two lengths are added together to get the quotient.

   I think of 4 times how many lengths of ten get me close to 7 tens in the whole: 1 ten. Then, 4 times how many lengths of ones gets me close to the remaining 36 ones: 9 ones.

G4-M3-Lesson 21

1. Yahya solved the following division problem by drawing an area model.

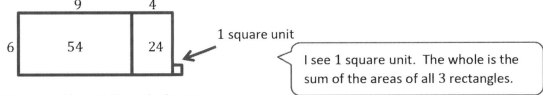

> I see 1 square unit. The whole is the sum of the areas of all 3 rectangles.

   a. What division problem did he solve? $79 \div 6$

   b. Show how Yahya's model can be represented using the distributive property.

$$(54 \div 6) + (24 \div 6)$$
$$= 9 + 4$$
$$= 13$$

> I remember to add a remainder of 1.

$$(6 \times 13) + 1 = 79$$

Solve the following problems using the area model. Support the area model with long division or the distributive property.

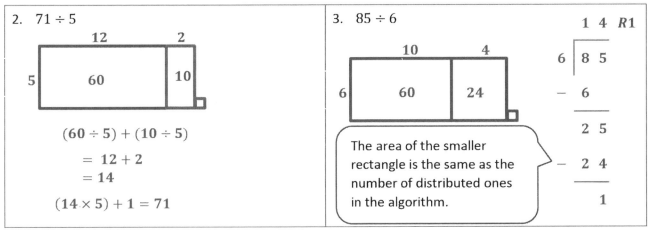

2. $71 \div 5$

$$(60 \div 5) + (10 \div 5)$$
$$= 12 + 2$$
$$= 14$$
$$(14 \times 5) + 1 = 71$$

3. $85 \div 6$

> The area of the smaller rectangle is the same as the number of distributed ones in the algorithm.

$$\begin{array}{r} 1\ 4\ R1 \\ 6\overline{\smash{)}8\ 5} \\ -\ 6 \\ \hline 2\ 5 \\ -\ 2\ 4 \\ \hline 1 \end{array}$$

4. Eighty-nine marbles were placed equally in 4 bags. How many marbles were in each bag? How many marbles are left over?

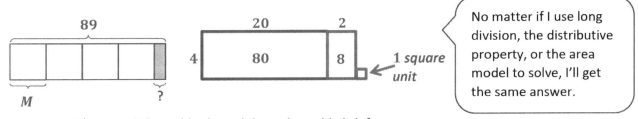

> No matter if I use long division, the distributive property, or the area model to solve, I'll get the same answer.

There are 22 marbles in each bag. 1 marble is left over.

Lesson 21:   Solve division problems with remainders using the area model.

G4-M3-Lesson 22

1. Record the factors of the given numbers as multiplication sentences and as a list in order from least to greatest. Classify each as prime (P) or composite (C).

	Multiplication Sentences	Factors	P or C
a.	5 $1 \times 5 = 5$	The factors of 5 are $1, 5$	P
b.	18 $1 \times 18 = 18$ $2 \times 9 = 18$ $3 \times 6 = 18$	The factors of 18 are $1, 2, 3, 6, 9, 18$	C

> I know a number is prime if it has only two factors. I know a number is composite if it has more than two factors.

2. Find all factors for the following number, and classify the number as prime or composite. Explain your classification of prime or composite.

Factor Pairs for 12	
1	12
2	6
3	4

12 is composite. I know that it is composite because it has more than two factors.

> I think of the multiplication facts that have a product of 12.

3. Jenny has 25 beads to divide evenly among 4 friends. She thinks there will be no leftovers. Use what you know about factor pairs to explain whether or not Jenny is correct.

Jenny is not correct. There will be leftovers. I know this because if 4 is one of the factors, there is no whole number that multiplies by 4 to get 25 as a product. There will be one bead left over.

> $4 \times 6 = 24$ and $4 \times 7 = 28$. There is no factor pair for 4 that results in a product of 25.

G4-M3-Lesson 23

1. Explain your thinking, or use division to answer the following.

Is 2 a factor of 96?	Is 3 a factor of 96?
Yes. 96 is an even number. 2 is a factor of every even number.	$$\begin{array}{r} 3\ \ 2 \\ 3\overline{\smash)9\ \ 6} \\ -\underline{9} \\ 0\ \ 6 \\ -\underline{\ 6} \\ 0 \end{array}$$ *Yes, 3 is a factor of 96. When I divide 96 by 3, my answer is 32.*
Is 4 a factor of 96?	Is 5 a factor of 96?
$$\begin{array}{r} 2\ \ 4 \\ 4\overline{\smash)9\ \ 6} \\ -\underline{8} \\ 1\ \ 6 \\ -\underline{1\ \ 6} \\ 0 \end{array}$$ *Yes, 4 is a factor of 96. When I divide 96 by 4, my answer is 24.*	*No, 5 is not a factor of 96. 96 does not have a 5 or 0 in the ones place. All numbers that have a 5 as a factor have a 5 or 0 in the ones place.*

I use what I know about factors to solve. Thinking about whether 2 is a factor or 5 is a factor is easy. Threes and fours are harder, so I divide to see if they are factors. 96 is divisible by both 3 and 4, so they are both factors of 96.

2. Use the associative property to find more factors of 28 and 32.

a. $28 = 14 \times 2$

    $= (\underline{\ 7\ } \times 2) \times 2$

    $= \underline{\ 7\ } \times (2 \times 2)$

    $= \underline{\ 7\ } \times 4$

    $= \underline{\ 28\ }$

b. $32 = \underline{\ 8\ } \times 4$

    $= (\underline{\ 2\ } \times 4) \times 4$

    $= \underline{\ 2\ } \times (4 \times 4)$

    $= \underline{\ 2\ } \times 16$

    $= \underline{\ 32\ }$

I find more factors of the whole number by breaking down one of the factors into smaller parts and then associating the factors differently using parentheses.

Lesson 23:   Use division and the associative property to test for factors and observe patterns.

EUREKA MATH™

3. In class, we used the associative property to show that when 6 is a factor, then 2 and 3 are factors, because $6 = 2 \times 3$. Use the fact that $12 = 2 \times 6$ to show that 2 and 6 are factors of 36, 48, and 60.

$36 = 12 \times 3$ $48 = 12 \times 4$ $60 = 12 \times 5$

$\quad = (2 \times 6) \times 3$ $\quad = (2 \times 6) \times 4$ $\quad = (2 \times 6) \times 5$

$\quad = 2 \times (6 \times 3)$ $\quad = 2 \times (6 \times 4)$ $\quad = 2 \times (6 \times 5)$

$\quad = 2 \times 18$ $\quad = 2 \times 24$ $\quad = 2 \times 30$

$\quad = 36$ $\quad = 48$ $\quad = 60$

I rewrite the number sentences, substituting 2×6 for 12. I can move the parentheses because of the associative property and then solve. This helps to show that both 2 and 6 are factors of 36, 48, and 60.

4. The first statement is false. The second statement is true. Explain why using words, pictures, or numbers.

> If a number has 2 and 8 as factors, then it has 16 as a factor.
> If a number has 16 as a factor, then both 2 and 8 are factors.

The first statement is false. For example, 8 has both 2 and 8 as factors, but it does not have 16 as a factor. The second statement is true. Any number that can be divided exactly by 16 can also be divided by 2 and 8 instead since $16 = 2 \times 8$. Example: $2 \times 16 = 32$

$$2 \times (2 \times 8) = 32$$

I give examples to help with my explanation.

G4-M3-Lesson 24

1. Write the multiples of 3 starting from 36. Time yourself for 1 minute. See how many multiples you can write.

    36, 39, 42, 45, 48, 51, 54, 57, 60, 63, 66, 69, 72, 75, 78, 81, 84, 87,

    90, 93, 96, 99, 102, 105, 108, 111, 114

    > I skip-count by threes starting with 36.

2. List the numbers that have 28 as a multiple.

    $1, 2, 4, 7, 14, 28$

    > This is just like finding the factor pairs of a number. If I say "28" when I skip-count by a number, that means 28 is a multiple of that number.

3. Use mental math, division, or the associative property to solve.

    a. Is 15 a multiple of 3? _yes_   Is 3 a factor of 15? _yes_

    > $3 \times 5 = 15$, so 3 is a factor of 15.

    b. Is 34 a multiple of 6? _no_   Is 6 a factor of 34? _no_

    c. Is 32 a multiple of 8? _yes_   Is 32 a factor of 8? _no_

    > If a number is a multiple of another number, it means that, when I skip-count, I say that number.

    > 8 is a factor of 32, but 32 is not a factor of 8.

Lesson 24:   Determine if a whole number is a multiple of another number.   **EUREKA MATH**

©2015 Great Minds. eureka-math.org
G4-M1-HWH-1.3.0-07.2015

4. Follow the directions below.

1	2	3	4	5	6	7	8	9	10
11	12	13	14	15	16	17	18	19	20
21	22	23	24	25	26	27	28	29	30
31	32	33	34	35	36	37	38	39	40
41	42	43	44	45	46	47	48	49	50
51	52	53	54	55	56	57	58	59	60
61	62	63	64	65	66	67	68	69	70
71	72	73	74	75	76	77	78	79	80
81	82	83	84	85	86	87	88	89	90
91	92	93	94	95	96	97	98	99	100

a. Circle the multiples of 10. When a number is a multiple of 10, what do you notice about the number in the ones place?

When a number is a multiple of 10, the number in the ones place is always a zero.

b. Draw a square around the multiples of 4. When a number is a multiple of 4, what are the possible numbers in the ones digit?

When a number is a multiple of 4, the possible number in the ones digit is 2, 4, 6, 8, or 0.

c. Put a triangle on the multiples of 3. Choose one. What do you notice about the sum of the digits? Choose another one. What do you notice about the sum of the digits?

15 → *The sum of the digits is 6.*

75 → *The sum of the digits is 12.*

If I look at more multiples of 3, I see that the sum of their digits is 3, 6, 9, 12, 15, or 18. Each of those numbers is a multiple of 3.

©2015 Great Minds. eureka-math.org
G4-M1-HWH-1.3.0-07.2015

G4-M3-Lesson 25

1. Follow the directions.

   Shade the number 1.

   a. Circle the first unmarked number.

   b. Cross off every multiple of that number except the one you circled. If it's already crossed off, skip it.

   c. Repeat Steps (a) and (b) until every number is either circled or crossed off.

   d. Shade every crossed out number.

1	②	3	4̸	5	6̸	7	8̸	9	1̸0̸
11	1̸2̸	13	1̸4̸	15	1̸6̸	17	1̸8̸	19	2̸0̸
21	2̸2̸	23	2̸4̸	25	2̸6̸	27	2̸8̸	29	3̸0̸
31	3̸2̸	33	3̸4̸	35	3̸6̸	37	3̸8̸	39	4̸0̸
41	4̸2̸	43	4̸4̸	45	4̸6̸	47	4̸8̸	49	5̸0̸
51	5̸2̸	53	5̸4̸	55	5̸6̸	57	5̸8̸	59	6̸0̸
61	6̸2̸	63	6̸4̸	65	6̸6̸	67	6̸8̸	69	7̸0̸
71	7̸2̸	73	7̸4̸	75	7̸6̸	77	7̸8̸	79	8̸0̸
81	8̸2̸	83	8̸4̸	85	8̸6̸	87	8̸8̸	89	9̸0̸
91	9̸2̸	93	9̸4̸	95	9̸6̸	97	9̸8̸	99	1̸0̸0̸

I cross off every multiple of 2 except for the number 2.

Lesson 25:   Explore properties of prime and composite numbers to 100 by using
                           multiples.

1	②	③	4̸	5	6̸	7	8̸	9̸	1̸0̸
11	1̸2̸	13	1̸4̸	1̸5̸	1̸6̸	17	1̸8̸	19	2̸0̸
2̸1̸	2̸2̸	23	2̸4̸	25	2̸6̸	2̸7̸	2̸8̸	29	3̸0̸
31	3̸2̸	3̸3̸	3̸4̸	35	3̸6̸	37	3̸8̸	3̸9̸	4̸0̸
41	4̸2̸	43	4̸4̸	4̸5̸	4̸6̸	47	4̸8̸	49	5̸0̸
5̸1̸	5̸2̸	53	5̸4̸	55	5̸6̸	5̸7̸	5̸8̸	59	6̸0̸
61	6̸2̸	6̸3̸	6̸4̸	65	6̸6̸	67	6̸8̸	6̸9̸	7̸0̸
71	7̸2̸	73	7̸4̸	7̸5̸	7̸6̸	77	7̸8̸	79	8̸0̸
8̸1̸	8̸2̸	83	8̸4̸	85	8̸6̸	8̸7̸	8̸8̸	89	9̸0̸
91	9̸2̸	9̸3̸	9̸4̸	95	9̸6̸	97	9̸8̸	9̸9̸	1̸0̸0̸

I circle 3 because it is the next number that is not circled or crossed off. I cross off every multiple of 3 except for the number 3. I skip-count by threes to find the multiples.

I continue the process, first for the multiples of 5 and then for the multiples of 7.

1	2	3	4	5	6	7	8	9	10
11	12	13	14	15	16	17	18	19	20
21	22	23	24	25	26	27	28	29	30
31	32	33	34	35	36	37	38	39	40
41	42	43	44	45	46	47	48	49	50
51	52	53	54	55	56	57	58	59	60
61	62	63	64	65	66	67	68	69	70
71	72	73	74	75	76	77	78	79	80
81	82	83	84	85	86	87	88	89	90
91	92	93	94	95	96	97	98	99	100

I circle 11 because 11 is the next number that is not circled or crossed off. I notice that every multiple of 11 is already crossed off.

I don't have to cross off the multiples of 13 because they are crossed off already.

I realize that when I circle any of the other numbers that are not already crossed off their multiples have already been crossed off.

I shade every crossed out number.

I see that this process helps me to find the numbers from 1 to 100 that are prime and the numbers from 1 to 100 that are composite.

EUREKA MATH

G4-M3-Lesson 26

1. Draw place value disks to represent the following problems. Rewrite each in unit form and solve.

a. $80 \div 4 =$ __20__

10   10   10   10   10   10   10   10

8 tens $\div 4 =$ _2 tens_

> 2 tens is the same as 20.

> I distribute 8 tens into 4 groups. There are 2 tens in each group.

b. $800 \div 4 =$ __200__

100   100   100   100   100   100   100   100

8 hundreds $\div 4 =$ _2 hundreds_

> I think of 800 in unit form as 8 hundreds.

> 8 hundreds divided equally into 4 groups is 2 hundreds.

c. $150 \div 3 =$ __50__

10 10 10 10 10   10 10 10 10 10   10 10 10 10 10

15 tens $\div 3 =$ _5 tens_

> I think of 150 as 1 hundred 5 tens, but that doesn't help me to divide because I can't partition a hundreds disk into 3 equal groups. To help me to divide, I think of 150 as 15 tens.

d. $1,500 \div 3 =$ __500__

100 100 100 100 100   100 100 100 100 100   100 100 100 100 100

15 hundreds $\div 3 =$ _5 hundreds_

> This is just like the last problem except the unit is hundreds instead of tens.

©2015 Great Minds. eureka-math.org
G4-M1-HWH-1.3.0-07.2015

2. Solve for the quotient. Rewrite each in unit form.

a. $900 \div 3 = 300$	b. $140 \div 2 = 70$	c. $1{,}500 \div 5 = 300$	d. $200 \div 5 = 40$
9 hundreds ÷ 3 = 3 hundreds	14 tens ÷ 2 = 7 tens	15 hundreds ÷ 5 = 3 hundreds	20 tens ÷ 5 = 4 tens

> These problems are very similar to what I just did. The difference is that I do not draw disks. I rewrite the numbers in unit form to help me solve.

3. An ice cream shop sold \$2,800 of ice cream in August, which was 4 times as much as was sold in May. How much ice cream was sold at the ice cream shop in May?

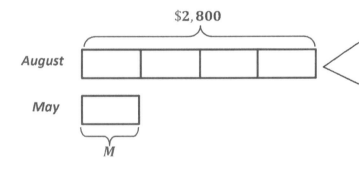

> I draw a tape diagram to show the ice cream sales for the month of August and the month of May. The tape for August is 4 times as long as the tape for May. 2,800 in unit form is 28 hundreds. If 4 units is 28 hundreds, 1 unit must be 28 hundreds ÷ 4. Since May is equal to 1 unit, the ice cream sales for May was \$700.

28 hundreds ÷ 4 = 7 hundreds

\$700 of ice cream was sold at the ice cream shop in May.

EUREKA
MATH

G4-M3-Lesson 27

Divide. Model using place value disks, and record using the algorithm.

$426 \div 3$

hundreds	tens	ones
● ● ● ●	● ●	● ● ● ● ● ●

I represent 426 as 4 hundreds 2 tens 6 ones.

I make space on the chart to distribute the disks into 3 equal groups.

hundreds	tens	ones
⌿ ⌿ ⌿ Ⓞ	● ●	● ● ● ● ● ●
●		
●		
●		

I remember from Lesson 16 to divide starting in the largest unit.

$$
\begin{array}{r}
1 \\
3\,)\,\overline{4\ \ 2\ \ 6} \\
-\ 3 \\
\hline
1
\end{array}
$$

4 hundreds divided by 3 is 1 hundred.

1 hundred in each group times 3 groups is 3 hundreds.

We started with 4 hundreds and evenly divided 3 hundreds. 1 hundred remains, which I've circled.

Lesson 27:   Represent and solve division problems with up to a three-digit dividend numerically and with place value disks requiring decomposing a remainder in the hundreds place.

37

©2015 Great Minds. eureka-math.org
G4-M1-HWH-1.3.0-07.2015

$$
\begin{array}{r}
1\\
3\,\overline{\big)\,4\ \ 2\ \ 6}\\
-\ \underline{3}\\
1\ \ 2
\end{array}
$$

> I remember from Lesson 17 that when there are remaining units that can't be divided, I decompose them as 10 of the next smallest unit. So 1 hundred is decomposed as 10 tens. Now there are 12 tens to divide.

> I continue to distribute tens and ones, and I record each step of the algorithm.

$$
\begin{array}{r}
1\ \ 4\ \ 2\\
3\,\overline{\big)\,4\ \ 2\ \ 6}\\
-\ \underline{3}\\
1\ \ 2\\
-\ \underline{1\ \ 2}\\
0\ \ 6\\
-\ \underline{6}\\
0
\end{array}
$$

} *1 hundred 4 tens 2 ones*

> The value in each group equals the quotient.

Lesson 27: Represent and solve division problems with up to a three-digit dividend numerically and with place value disks requiring decomposing a remainder in the hundreds place.

©2015 Great Minds. eureka-math.org
G4-M1-HWH-1.3.0-07.2015

EUREKA
MATH

G4-M3-Lesson 28

1. Divide. Check your work by multiplying. Draw disks on a place value chart as needed.

    a. $217 \div 4$

hundreds	tens	ones

Quotient $= 54$

Remainder $= 1$

$$\begin{array}{r} 5\ \ 4 \\ \times\ \ \ \ 4 \\ \hline 2\ \ 1\ \ 6 \end{array}$$

$$\begin{array}{r} 2\ \ 1\ \ 6 \\ +\ \ \ \ \ \ 1 \\ \hline 2\ \ 1\ \ 7 \end{array}$$

} 5 tens 4 ones

I check my answer by multiplying the quotient and the divisor, and then I add the remainder. My answer of 217 matches the whole in the division expression.

I can't distribute 2 hundreds evenly among the 4 groups. I decompose each hundred as 10 tens. Now I have 21 tens.

    b. $743 \div 3$

$$\begin{array}{r} 2\ \ 4\ \ 7\ \ R2 \\ 3\ \overline{)\ 7\ \ 4\ \ 3} \\ -\ 6\ \ \ \ \ \ \ \\ \hline 1\ \ 4\ \ \ \ \\ -\ 1\ \ 2\ \ \ \ \\ \hline 2\ \ 3 \\ -\ 2\ \ 1 \\ \hline 2 \end{array}$$

$$\begin{array}{r} 2\ \ 4\ \ 7 \\ \times\ \ \ \ \ 3 \\ \hline 7\ \ 4\ \ 1 \end{array}$$

$$\begin{array}{r} 7\ \ 4\ \ 1 \\ +\ \ \ \ \ 2 \\ \hline 7\ \ 4\ \ 3 \end{array}$$

I visualize each step on the place value chart as I record the steps of the algorithm.

EUREKA MATH   **Lesson 28:**   Represent and solve three-digit dividend division with divisors of 2, 3, 4, and 5 numerically.   39

©2015 Great Minds. eureka-math.org
G4-M1-HWH-1.3.0-07.2015

2. Constance ran 620 meters around the 4 sides of a square field. How many meters long was each side of the field?

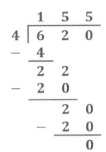   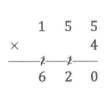

620 meters

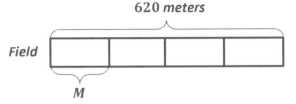

Field

Each side of the field was 155 meters.

Lesson 28:   Represent and solve three-digit dividend division with divisors of 2, 3, 4, and 5 numerically.

EUREKA
MATH

G4-M3-Lesson 29

1. Divide, and then check using multiplication.

   $3,268 \div 4$

```
         8  1  7
   4 | 3, 2  6  8
     − 3  2
        0  6
       −   4
          2  8
        − 2  8
             0
```

> I divide just as I learned to in Lessons 16, 17, 27, and 28. The challenge now is that the whole is larger, so I record the steps of the algorithm using long division and not using the place value chart.

```
        8  1  7
   ×           4
        1
   3,   2  6  8
```

> I check the answer by multiplying the quotient and the divisor. The product is equal to the whole.

2. A school buys 3 boxes of pencils. Each box has an equal number of pencils. There are 4,272 pencils altogether. How many pencils are in 2 boxes?

   4,272

   Pencils [? | |]
                  P

> 3 units are equal to 4,272 pencils. I need to solve for how many pencils are in 2 units.

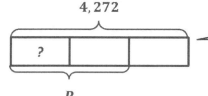

```
      1, 4  2  4
   3 | 4, 2  7  2
     − 3
       1  2
     − 1  2
          0  7
        −    6
             1  2
           − 1  2
                0
```

```
     1, 4  2  4
   ×          2
     2, 8  4  8
```

There are 2,848 pencils in 2 boxes.

> I multiply by 2 to determine how many pencils are in 2 units.

> I find how many pencils are in 1 unit by dividing 4,272 by 3. There are 1,424 pencils in 1 unit.

EUREKA
MATH™

Lesson 29:   Represent numerically four-digit dividend division with divisors of 2, 3,
             4, and 5, decomposing a remainder up to three times.

41

©2015 Great Minds. eureka-math.org
G4-M1-HWH-1.3.0-07.2015

G4-M3-Lesson 30

Divide. Check your solutions by multiplying.

1. 705 ÷ 2

```
      3  5  2  R1
   2 | 7  0  5
   -  6
      1  0
   -  1  0
         0  5
      -     4
            1
```

> I decompose 1 hundred as 10 tens. There are no other tens to distribute. So I keep dividing, this time in the tens.

> Once I divide the 10 tens, there are no tens remaining. But I must keep dividing. There are still 5 ones to divide.

```
         3  5  2
   ×           2
   ──────────────
         7  0  4
```

```
         7  0  4
   +           1
   ──────────────
         7  0  5
```

2. 6,250 ÷ 5

```
      1  2  5  0
   5 | 6, 2  5  0
   -  5
      1  2
   -  1  0
         2  5
      -  2  5
            0  0
         -     0
               0
```

> This time when I divide, there are no ones to distribute. 0 ones divided by 5 is 0 ones. I place a 0 in the ones place of the quotient to show that there are no ones.

```
      1, 2  5  0
   ×           5
   ──────────────
      6, 2  5  0
```

3. 3,220 ÷ 4

```
         8  0  5
   4 | 3, 2  2  0
   -  3  2
         0  2
      -     0
            2  0
         -  2  0
               0
```

> 2 tens can't be evenly divided by 4, so I record 0 tens in the quotient. But I must continue the steps of the algorithm: 0 tens times 4 equals 0 tens. 2 tens minus 0 tens is 2 tens.

```
         8  0  5
   ×           4
   ──────────────
      3, 2  2  0
```

Lesson 30:   Solve division problems with a zero in the dividend or with a zero in the quotient.

G4-M3-Lesson 31

Solve the following problems. Draw tape diagrams to help you solve. Identify if the group size or the number of groups is unknown.

1. 700 liters of water was shared equally among 4 aquariums. How many liters of water does each aquarium have?

700 *liters*

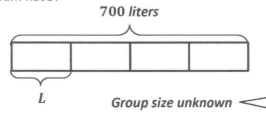

L   *Group size unknown*

> I draw a tape diagram to show 4 aquariums. I need to find the value of each aquarium, or the size of the group.

```
      1  7  5
  4 | 7  0  0
  -  4
      3  0
  -   2  8
         2  0
  -      2  0
            0
```

> I divide 700 by 4 to find the value of 1 aquarium, or group.

Each aquarium has 175 liters of water.

2. Emma separated 824 donuts into boxes. Each box contained 4 donuts. How many boxes of donuts did Emma fill?

824

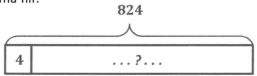

4   . . . ? . . .

Number of groups unknown

> I do not know how many boxes were filled. I show one group of 4. I draw three dots, a question mark, and three dots to indicate that the groups of 4 continue. The number of groups is unknown.

```
      2  0  6
  4 | 8  2  4
  -  8
      0  2
  -    0
         2  4
  -      2  4
            0
```

Emma filled 206 boxes of donuts.

> I divide 824 by 4 to find the number of groups.

EUREKA MATH   **Lesson 31:**   Interpret division word problems as either *number of groups unknown*   **43**
                                 or *group size unknown*.

©2015 Great Minds. eureka-math.org
G4-M1-HWH-1.3.0-07.2015

G4-M3-Lesson 32

Solve the following problems. Draw tape diagrams to help you solve. If there is a remainder, shade in a small portion of the tape diagram to represent that portion of the whole.

1. The clown has 1,649 balloons. It takes 8 balloons to make a balloon animal. How many balloon animals can the clown make?

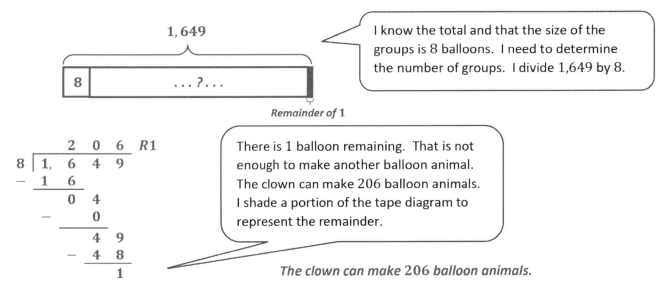

I know the total and that the size of the groups is 8 balloons. I need to determine the number of groups. I divide 1,649 by 8.

There is 1 balloon remaining. That is not enough to make another balloon animal. The clown can make 206 balloon animals. I shade a portion of the tape diagram to represent the remainder.

The clown can make 206 balloon animals.

2. In 7 days, Cassidy threw a total of 609 pitches. If she threw the same number of pitches each day, how many pitches did she throw in one day?

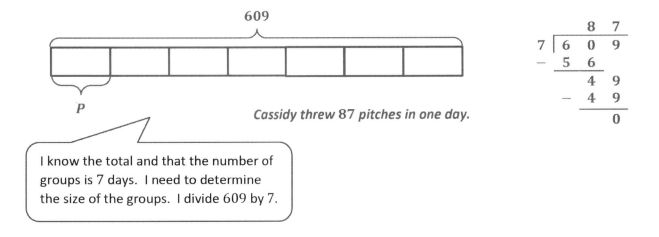

Cassidy threw 87 pitches in one day.

I know the total and that the number of groups is 7 days. I need to determine the size of the groups. I divide 609 by 7.

EUREKA MATH™

©2015 Great Minds. eureka-math.org
G4-M1-HWH-1.3.0-07.2015

G4-M3-Lesson 33

1. Tyler solved a division problem by drawing this area model.

	300	50	9
4	1,200	200	36

> The total area is $1,200 + 200 + 36 = 1,436$. The width is 4. The length is $300 + 50 + 9 = 359$. $A \div w = l$.

a. What division problem did he solve?

Tyler solved $1,436 \div 4 = 359$.

b. Show a number bond to represent Tyler's area model, and represent the total length using the distributive property.

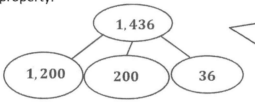

> My number bond shows the same whole and parts as the area model. To represent the length, I divide each of the smaller areas by the width of 4.

$$(1,200 \div 4) + (200 \div 4) + (36 \div 4)$$
$$= \quad 300 \quad + \quad 50 \quad + \quad 9$$
$$= \quad 359$$

2.

a. Draw an area model to solve $591 \div 3$.

	100	90	7
3	300	270	21

> I decompose the area of 591 into smaller parts that are easy to divide by 3. I start with the hundreds. I distribute 3 hundreds. The area remaining to distribute is 291. I distribute 27 tens. The area remaining to distribute is 21 ones. I distribute the ones. I have a side length of $100 + 90 + 7 = 197$.

$591 \div 3 = 197$

> 3 hundreds, 27 tens, and 21 ones are all multiples of 3, which is the width and divisor.

EUREKA MATH™   **Lesson 33:** Explain the connection of the area model of division to the long division algorithm for three- and four-digit dividends.   45

©2015 Great Minds. eureka-math.org
G4-M1-HWH-1.3.0-07.2015

b. Draw a number bond to represent this problem.

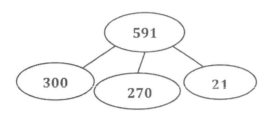

$(300 \div 3) + (270 \div 3) + (21 \div 3)$

$= \quad 100 \quad + \quad 90 \quad + \quad 7$

$= \quad 197$

My number bond shows the same whole and parts as the area model. To represent the length, I divide each of the smaller areas by the width of 3. I get $100 + 90 + 7 = 197$.

c. Record your work using the long division algorithm.

```
        1  9  7
    3 | 5  9  1
    -   3
      ─────
        2  9
    -   2  7
      ─────
           2  1
    -      2  1
         ─────
              0
```

Lesson 33:   Explain the connection of the area model of division to the long division
               algorithm for three- and four-digit dividends.

**EUREKA
MATH**

G4-M3-Lesson 34

1. Use the associative property to rewrite each expression. Solve using disks, and then complete the number sentences.

I rename 30 as (3×10), and then I group the factor of 10 with 27.

I draw 2 tens 7 ones. I show 10 times as many by shifting the disks one place to the left.

30×27

$= (3 \times 10) \times \underline{27}$

$= 3 \times (10 \times \underline{27})$

$= \underline{810}$

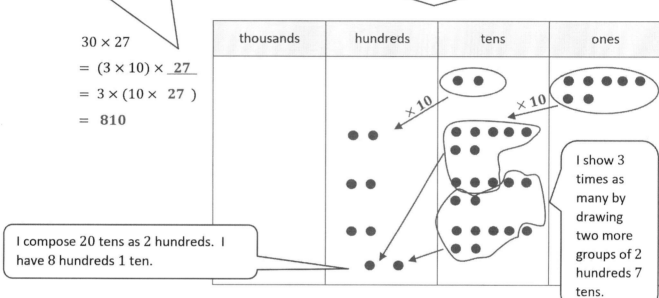

I compose 20 tens as 2 hundreds. I have 8 hundreds 1 ten.

I show 3 times as many by drawing two more groups of 2 hundreds 7 tens.

thousands	hundreds	tens	ones

2. Use the associative property and place value disks to solve.

thousands	hundreds	tens	ones

20×28

$= (2 \times 10) \times 28$

$= 2 \times (10 \times 28)$

$= 560$

By decomposing 20 into 2 and 10, I think about the product being twice as much as 28 tens.

3. Use the associative property without place value disks to solve.

60×54

$= (6 \times 10) \times 54$

$= 6 \times (10 \times 54)$

$= 3,240$

$$\begin{array}{r} 5 \quad 4 \quad 0 \\ \times \qquad 6 \\ \hline 3, \quad 2 \quad 4 \quad 0 \end{array}$$

> I rename 60 as 6 × 10. Ten times as many as 54 ones is 54 tens. I multiply 6 times 540.

4. Use the distributive property to solve the following. Distribute the second factor.

40×56

$= (40 \times 50) + (40 \times 6)$

$= 2,000 + 240$

$= 2,240$

> I use unit language to help me solve mentally. Four tens times 5 tens is 20 hundreds. And 4 tens times 6 ones is 24 tens.

Lesson 34: Multiply two-digit multiples of 10 by two-digit numbers using a place value chart.

EUREKA MATH

©2015 Great Minds. eureka-math.org
G4-M1-HWH-1.3.0-07.2015

G4-M3-Lesson 35

1. Use an area model to represent the following expression. Then, record the partial products vertically and solve.

40×27

> I write 40 as the width and decompose 27 as 20 and 7 for the length.

	20	7
40	40×20 4 *tens* × 2 *tens* 8 *hundreds* **800**	40×7 4 *tens* × 7 *ones* 28 *tens* **280**

> I solve for each of the smaller areas.

$$
\begin{array}{r}
2\ 7 \\
\times\ \ 4\ 0 \\
\hline
2\ 8\ 0 \\
+\ 8\ 0\ 0 \\
\hline
1,\ 0\ 8\ 0
\end{array}
$$

> I record the partial products. The partial products have the same value as the areas of the smaller rectangles.

2. Visualize the area model, and solve the following expression numerically.

30×66

$$
\begin{array}{r}
6\ 6 \\
\times\ \ 3\ 0 \\
\hline
1\ 8\ 0 \\
+\ 1,\ 8\ 0\ 0 \\
\hline
1,\ 9\ 8\ 0
\end{array}
$$

> To solve, I visualize the area model. I see the width as 30 and the length as $60 + 6$. 3 tens × 6 ones = 18 tens. 3 tens × 6 tens = 18 hundreds. I record the partial products. I find the total. $180 + 1,800 = 1,980$.

G4-M3-Lesson 36

1.

a. In each of the two models pictured below, write the expressions that determine the area of each of the four smaller rectangles.

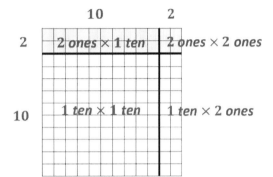

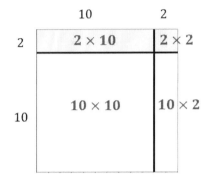

> I write the expressions that determine the area of each of the four smaller rectangles. The area of each smaller rectangle is equal to its width times its length. I can write the expressions in unit form or standard form.

b. Using the distributive property, rewrite the area of the large rectangle as the sum of the areas of the four smaller rectangles. Express the area first in number form and then read it in unit form.

$$12 \times 12 = (2 \times \underline{2}) + (2 \times \underline{10}) + (10 \times \underline{2}) + (10 \times \underline{10})$$

> I write the expressions of the areas of the four smaller rectangles. I use the area models to help me. I say, "12 × 12 = (2 ones × 2 ones) + (2 ones × 1 ten) + (1 ten × 2 ones) + (1 ten × 1 ten)."

EUREKA MATH

2. Use an area model to represent the following expression. Record the partial products vertically and solve.

15×33

	30	**3**
5	5 ones × 3 tens	5 ones × 3 ones
10	1 ten × 3 tens	1 ten × 3 ones

$$
\begin{array}{r}
3\ 3 \\
\times\ \ 1\ 5 \\
\hline
1\ 5 \\
1\ 5\ 0 \\
3\ 0 \\
+\ 3\ 0\ 0 \\
\hline
4\ 9\ 5
\end{array}
$$

I write the expressions that represent the areas of the four smaller rectangles. I record each partial product vertically. I find the sum of the areas of the four smaller rectangles.

3. Visualize the area model, and solve the following numerically using four partial products. (You may sketch an area model if it helps.)

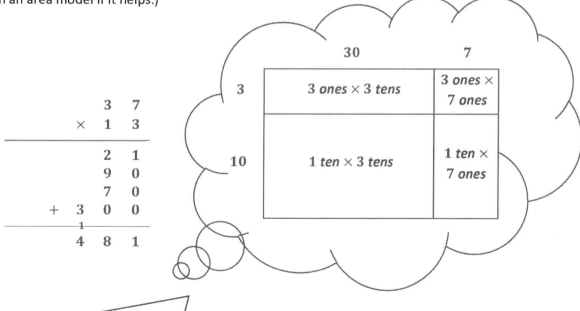

$$
\begin{array}{r}
3\ 7 \\
\times\ \ 1\ 3 \\
\hline
2\ 1 \\
9\ 0 \\
7\ 0 \\
+\ 3\ 0\ 0 \\
\hline
{\scriptstyle 1}\ \\
4\ 8\ 1
\end{array}
$$

	30	**7**
3	3 ones × 3 tens	3 ones × 7 ones
10	1 ten × 3 tens	1 ten × 7 ones

To solve, I visualize the area model. I record the partial products. I find the total.

G4-M3-Lesson 37

1. Solve 37 × 54 using 4 partial products and 2 partial products. Remember to think in terms of units as you solve. Write an expression to find the area of each smaller rectangle in the area model. Match each partial product to its area on the models.

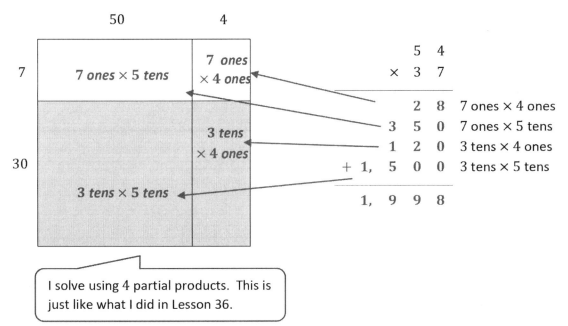

I solve using 4 partial products. This is just like what I did in Lesson 36.

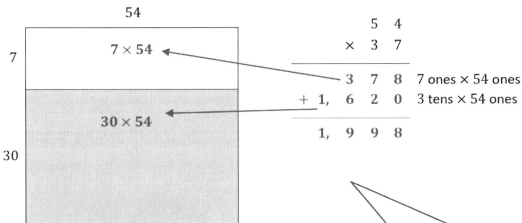

To show 2 partial products, I combine the values of the top two rectangles, and I combine the values of the bottom two rectangles.

I know one partial product is represented by the white portion of the large rectangle. The other partial product is represented by the shaded portion.

2. Solve 38 × 46 using 2 partial products and an area model. Match each partial product to its area on the model.

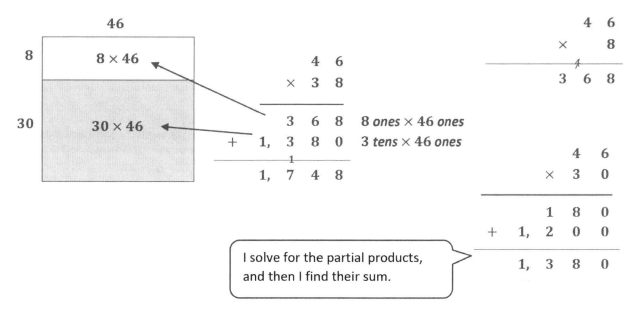

I solve for the partial products, and then I find their sum.

3. Solve the following using 2 partial products. Visualize the area model to help you.

$$
\begin{array}{r}
7\ 4 \\
\times\ \ 2\ 5 \\
\hline
3\ 7\ 0 \\
+\ 1,\ 4\ 8\ 0 \\
\hline
1,\ 8\ 5\ 0
\end{array}
$$

$5 × 74$
$20 × 74$

I visualize the 2 partial products of 5 ones × 74 and 2 tens × 74. I solve for the partial products and then find their sum.

$$
\begin{array}{r}
7\ 4 \\
\times\ \ \ \ 5 \\
\hline
3\ 7\ 0
\end{array}
$$

$$
\begin{array}{r}
7\ 4 \\
\times\ \ 2\ 0 \\
\hline
8\ 0 \\
+\ 1,\ 4\ 0\ 0 \\
\hline
1,\ 4\ 8\ 0
\end{array}
$$

EUREKA MATH™   **Lesson 37:**   Transition from four partial products to the standard algorithm for two-digit by two-digit multiplication.   53

©2015 Great Minds. eureka-math.org
G4-M1-HWH-1.3.0-07.2015

G4-M3-Lesson 38

1. Express 38 × 53 as two partial products using the distributive property. Solve.

```
        53
   ┌──────────────┐
 8 │   8 × 53     │
   ├──────────────┤
   │              │
30 │   30 × 53    │
   │              │
   └──────────────┘
```

38 × 53 = (**8** fifty-threes) + (**30** fifty-threes)

```
              5   3
          ×   3   8
        ─────────────
          4   2   4      8  × 53
      +  1, 5   9   0   30  × 53
          1   1
        ─────────────
          2,  0   1   4
```

> I can solve for each of the partial products and find their sum to verify that I solved the 2-digit by 2-digit algorithm correctly.

```
        5   3
    ×       8
  ───────────
    4   2   4
```

```
            5   3
        ×   3   0
      ───────────
            9   0
    +   1,  5   0   0
      ───────────
        1,  5   9   0
```

2. Express 34 × 44 as two partial products using the distributive property. Solve.

```
        44
   ┌──────────────┐
 4 │   4 × 44     │
   ├──────────────┤
   │              │
30 │   30 × 44    │
   │              │
   └──────────────┘
```

34 × 44 = (**4** × **44**) + (**30** × **44**)

```
            4   4
        ×   3   4
      ───────────
        1   7   6      4  × 44
    +  1, 3   2   0   30  × 44
      ───────────
        1,  4   9   6
```

```
        4   4
    ×       4
  ───────────
    1   7   6
```

```
            4   4
        ×   3   0
      ───────────
        1   2   0
    +  1,  2   0   0
      ───────────
        1,  3   2   0
```

Lesson 38:   Transition from four partial products to the standard algorithm
                          for two-digit by two-digit multiplication.

©2015 Great Minds. eureka-math.org
G4-M1-HWH-1.3.0-07.2015

3. Solve the following using two partial products.

```
              6   2
        ×     4   3
       ─────────────
              1   8   6        3  ×  62
    +    2,   4   8   0       40  ×  62
                  1
       ─────────────
         2,   6   6   6
```

I think of 3 sixty-twos + 40 sixty-twos.

4. Solve using the multiplication algorithm.

    62 × 36

```
              3   6
        ×     6   2
       ─────────────
                  1
              7   2
              3
    +    2,   1   6   0
                  1
       ─────────────
         2,   2   3   2
```

2 ones × 6 ones = 12 ones. I represent 12 ones as 1 ten 2 ones.

2 ones × 3 tens = 6 tens. 6 tens + 1 ten = 7 tens. I cross off 1 ten to show that I add it to 6 tens.

6 tens × 6 ones = 36 tens. I represent 36 tens as 3 hundreds 6 tens 0 ones.

6 tens × 3 tens = 18 hundreds. 18 hundreds + 3 hundreds = 21 hundreds. I cross off 3 hundreds to show that I add it to 18 hundreds.

EUREKA MATH™   **Lesson 38:** Transition from four partial products to the standard algorithm for two-digit by two-digit multiplication.   **55**

©2015 Great Minds. eureka-math.org
G4-M1-HWH-1.3.0-07.2015

Homework Helpers

Grade 4
Module 4

G4-M4-Lesson 1

1. Use the following directions to draw a figure in the box below.

    a. Draw two points: J and K.

    b. Use a straightedge to draw $\overleftrightarrow{JK}$. —— I read this as "line JK."

    c. Draw a new point that is on $\overleftrightarrow{JK}$. Label it L.

    d. Draw a point not on $\overleftrightarrow{JK}$. Label it M.

    e. Construct $\overline{LM}$. —— I read this as "line segment LM."

    f. Use the points you've already labeled to name two angles. $\angle JLM, \angle MLK$

    g. Identify the angles you've labeled by drawing an arc to indicate the position of the angles.

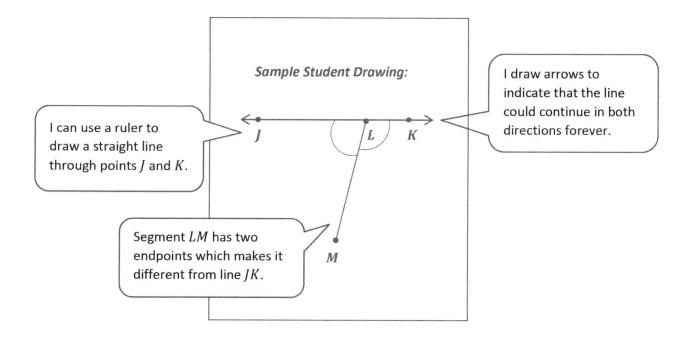

I can use a ruler to draw a straight line through points J and K.

I draw arrows to indicate that the line could continue in both directions forever.

Sample Student Drawing:

Segment LM has two endpoints which makes it different from line JK.

EUREKA
MATH™

Lesson 1:   Identify and draw points, lines, line segments, rays, and angles.
            Recognize them in various contexts and familiar figures.

1

©2015 Great Minds. eureka-math.org
G4-M1-HWH-1.3.0-07.2015

2.

a. Observe the familiar figures below. Label some points on each figure.

b. Use those points to label and name representations of each of the following in the table below: ray, line, line segment, and angle. Extend segments to show lines and rays.

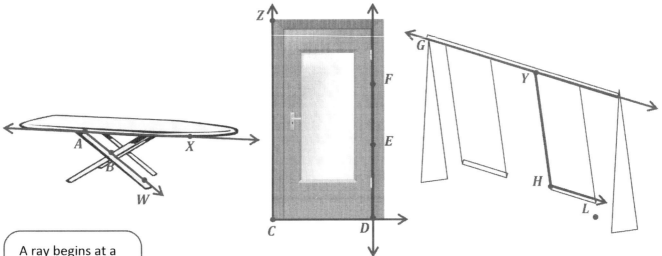

A ray begins at a point and extends indefinitely in one direction.

	Ironing Board	Door	Swing Set
Ray	$\overrightarrow{AW}$	$\overrightarrow{CD}$	$\overrightarrow{HL}$
Line	$\overleftrightarrow{AX}$	$\overleftrightarrow{DF}$	$\overleftrightarrow{GY}$
Line Segment	$\overline{AB}$	$\overline{EF}$	$\overline{YH}$
Angle	$\angle WAX$	$\angle ZCD$	$\angle YHL$

I write symbols for angle ($\angle$), segment ($\frown$), ray ($\frown$), and line ($\overleftrightarrow{}$).

Lesson 1:   Identify and draw points, lines, line segments, rays, and angles.
                        Recognize them in various contexts and familiar figures.

EUREKA MATH™

G4-M4-Lesson 2

> I can remake a right angle template using a circle of paper. I fold it into fourths and use the square corner.

1. Use the right angle template that you made in class to determine if each of the following angles is greater than, less than, or equal to a right angle. Label each as *greater than, less than,* or *equal to,* and then connect each angle to the correct label of acute, right, or obtuse.

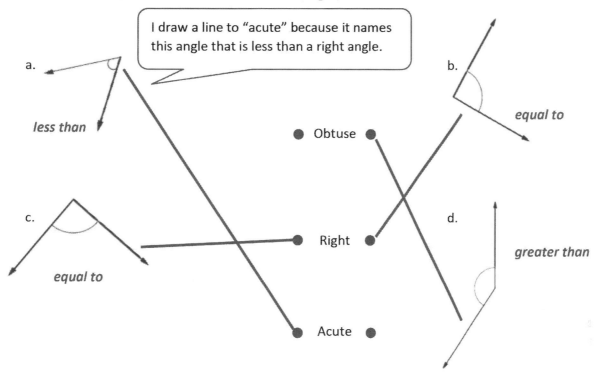

> I draw a line to "acute" because it names this angle that is less than a right angle.

a.

less than

b.

equal to

● Obtuse ●

c.

d.

● Right ●

greater than

equal to

● Acute ●

2. Construct an obtuse angle using a straightedge and the right angle template that you created. Explain the characteristics of an obtuse angle by comparing it to a right angle. Use the words *greater than, less than,* or *equal to* in your explanation.

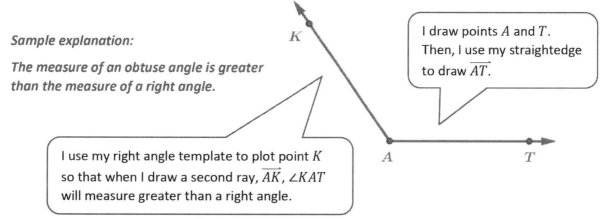

Sample explanation:

The measure of an obtuse angle is greater than the measure of a right angle.

> I draw points A and T. Then, I use my straightedge to draw $\overrightarrow{AT}$.

> I use my right angle template to plot point K so that when I draw a second ray, $\overrightarrow{AK}$, $\angle KAT$ will measure greater than a right angle.

Lesson 2:   Use right angles to determine whether angles are equal to, greater than, or less than right angles. Draw right, obtuse, and acute angles.

3

©2015 Great Minds. eureka-math.org
G4-M1-HWH-1.3.0-07.2015

G4-M4-Lesson 3

1. On each object, trace at least one pair of lines that appear to be perpendicular.

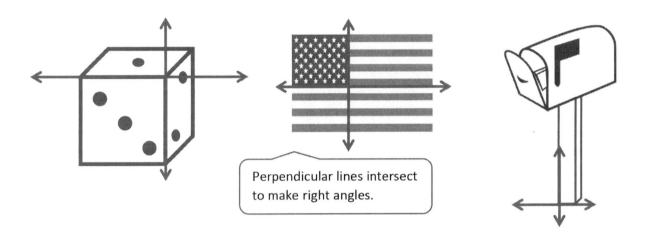

Perpendicular lines intersect to make right angles.

2. In the grid below, draw a segment that is perpendicular to the given segment. Use a straightedge.

I can turn the paper to make the diagonal segment horizontal, if that helps.

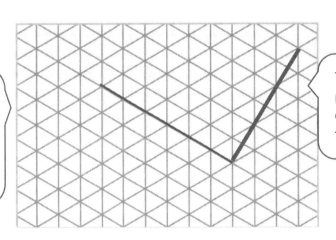

The segment perpendicular to this diagonal cuts the triangles in half.

EUREKA MATH™

3. Use the right angle template that you created in class to determine if the following figure has a right angle. If so, mark it with a small square. For each right angle you find, name the corresponding perpendicular sides.

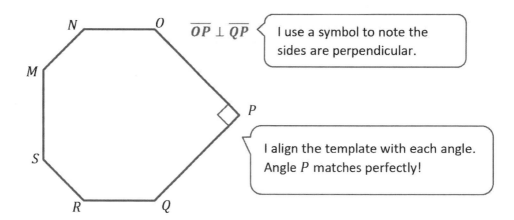

$\overline{OP} \perp \overline{QP}$ — I use a symbol to note the sides are perpendicular.

I align the template with each angle. Angle P matches perfectly!

G4-M4-Lesson 4

1. On each object, trace at least one pair of lines that appear to be parallel.

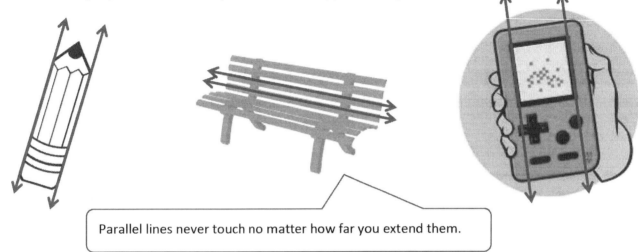

Parallel lines never touch no matter how far you extend them.

2. In the grid below, use a straightedge to draw a segment that is parallel to the given segment.

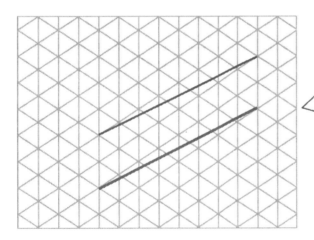

It's tricky to draw diagonal parallel line segments! I draw a line segment that is a distance of two triangle base lengths at every point along the segment.

3. Draw a line using your straightedge. Then, use your right angle template and straightedge to construct a line parallel to the first line you drew.

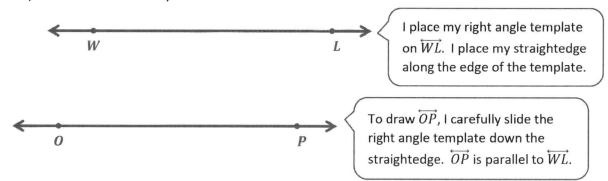

I place my right angle template on $\overleftrightarrow{WL}$. I place my straightedge along the edge of the template.

To draw $\overleftrightarrow{OP}$, I carefully slide the right angle template down the straightedge. $\overleftrightarrow{OP}$ is parallel to $\overleftrightarrow{WL}$.

G4-M4-Lesson 5

1. Identify the measures of the following angles.

    The angle measures 80°.

    To measure an angle, I place the protractor on the angle so that one of the rays aligns to zero and the vertex is at the center of the protractor. I read the number aligned with the second ray to determine the measure of the angle.

    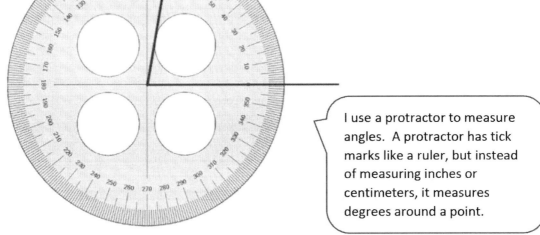

    I use a protractor to measure angles. A protractor has tick marks like a ruler, but instead of measuring inches or centimeters, it measures degrees around a point.

2. If you didn't have a protractor, how could you construct one? Use words, pictures, or numbers to explain in the space below.

    Sample Student Response:

    If I didn't have a protractor, I could cut out a paper circle. Using a right angle template, I could partition the circle in fourths and then mark 0°, 90°, 180°, 270°, and 360°. Although my protractor would not be able to give an exact measurement of any angle, I could estimate the measure using these benchmarks.

    I reflect on my experiences and discussions in class. We partitioned paper circles in various ways, labeling degrees accurately.

Lesson 5:   Use a circular protractor to understand a 1-degree angle as $\frac{1}{360}$ of a turn. Explore benchmark angles using the protractor.

©2015 Great Minds. eureka-math.org
G4-M1-HWH-1.3.0-07.2015

EUREKA MATH

G4-M4-Lesson 6

1. Use a protractor to measure the angle, and then record the measurement in degrees.

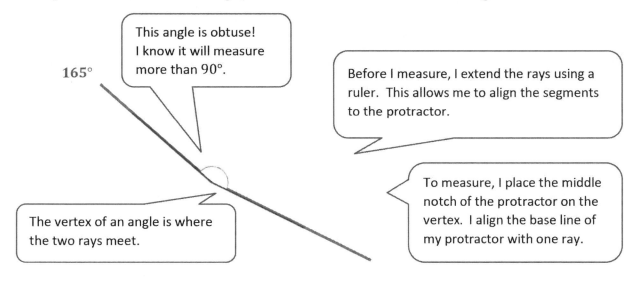

165°

This angle is obtuse! I know it will measure more than 90°.

Before I measure, I extend the rays using a ruler. This allows me to align the segments to the protractor.

The vertex of an angle is where the two rays meet.

To measure, I place the middle notch of the protractor on the vertex. I align the base line of my protractor with one ray.

2. Use a protractor to measure the angle. Extend the length of the segments as needed. When you extend the segments, does the angle measure stay the same? Explain how you know.

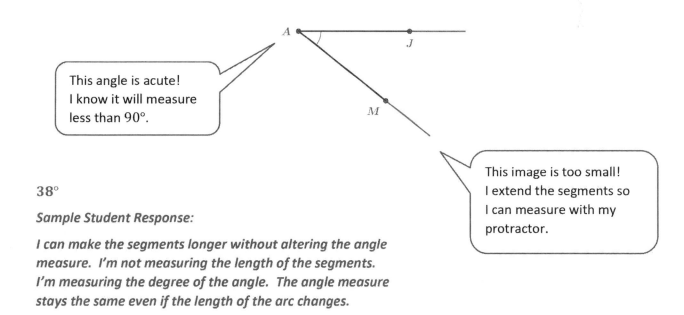

This angle is acute! I know it will measure less than 90°.

This image is too small! I extend the segments so I can measure with my protractor.

38°

Sample Student Response:

I can make the segments longer without altering the angle measure. I'm not measuring the length of the segments. I'm measuring the degree of the angle. The angle measure stays the same even if the length of the arc changes.

Lesson 6:   Use varied protractors to distinguish angle measure from length measurement.

©2015 Great Minds. eureka-math.org
G4-M1-HWH-1.3.0-07.2015

9

G4-M4-Lesson 7

Construct angles that measure the give number of degrees. For the first problem, use the ray shown as one of the rays of the angle with its endpoint as the vertex of the angle. Draw an arc to indicate the angle that was measured.

1. 90°

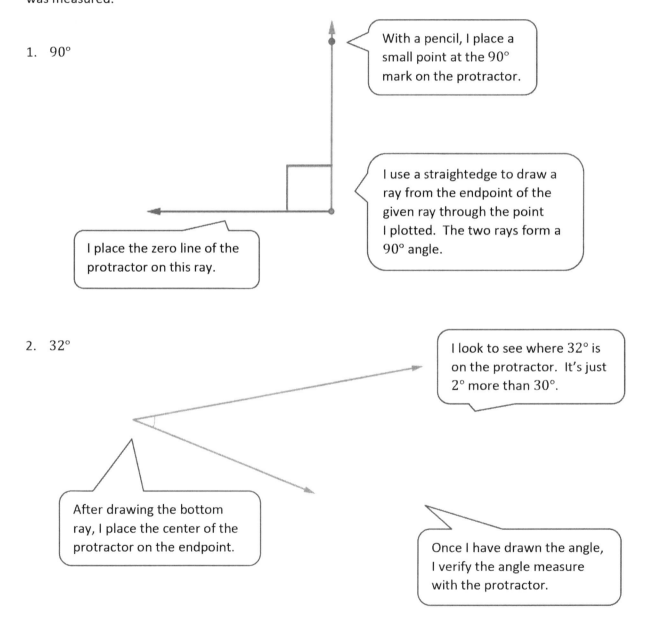

With a pencil, I place a small point at the 90° mark on the protractor.

I use a straightedge to draw a ray from the endpoint of the given ray through the point I plotted. The two rays form a 90° angle.

I place the zero line of the protractor on this ray.

2. 32°

I look to see where 32° is on the protractor. It's just 2° more than 30°.

After drawing the bottom ray, I place the center of the protractor on the endpoint.

Once I have drawn the angle, I verify the angle measure with the protractor.

Lesson 7:   Measure and draw angles. Sketch given angle measures, and verify with
                          a protractor.

G4-M4-Lesson 8

1. James looked at the clock when he put the cake in the oven and when he took it out. How many degrees did the minute hand turn from start to finish?

start time

end time

The minute hand turned 180°.

I know from Lesson 5 that there are 360° in a full turn. From the 12 to the 3 is a 90° angle, and from the 3 to the 6 is another 90° angle.

2. Delonte turned the lock on his locker one quarter turn to the right and then 180° to the left. Draw a picture showing the position of the lock after he turned it.

before

after

I think of the lock as a clock. A quarter-turn to the right is 15 minutes, and 180° to the left is 30 minutes backward.

3. How many quarter-turns does the picture need to be rotated in order for it to be upright?

To be upright, the picture needs to be turned two quarter-turns.

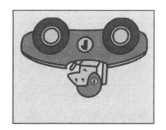

I can turn the paper itself to help me figure out the answer!

G4-M4-Lesson 9

Pattern Blocks

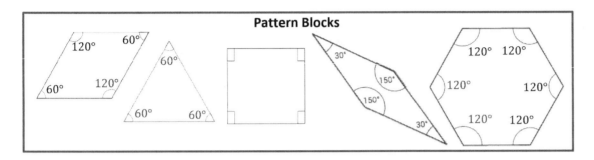

1. Sketch one way to compose ∠ABC using two or more pattern blocks. Write an addition sentence to show how you composed the given angle.

∠ABC = 150°

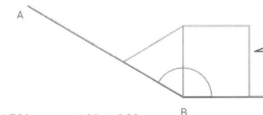

> I use a triangle and a square. I add the measure of each angle: 60° + 90° = 150°.

150° = ___**60° + 90°**___

2. Sabrina built the following shape with her pattern blocks. As indicated by their arcs, solve for x°, y°, and z°. Write an addition sentence for each. The first one is done for you.

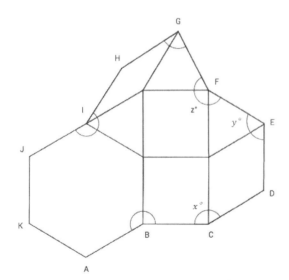

a. $y° = 60° + 60°$

$y° = 120°$

b. $z° = $ ___**60° + 90° + 60°**___

$z° = $ ___**210°**___

c. $x° = $ ___**90° + 60°**___

$x° = $ ___**150°**___

> To determine x°, y°, and z°, I add together the smaller angles encompassed by the arcs. I use the chart at the top of the page to determine the measure of each of the smaller angles.

G4-M4-Lesson 10

1. Write an equation, and solve for the measurement of ∠x. Verify the measurement using a protractor.

   a. ∠JKL is a straight angle.

   b. Solve for the measurement of ∠USW. ∠RST is a straight angle.

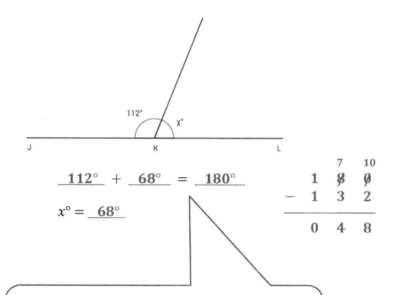

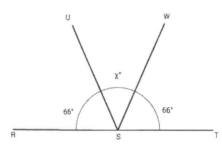

$$112° + 68° = 180°$$

$$x° = 68°$$

$$
\begin{array}{r}
7\ 10 \\
1\ \cancel{8}\ \cancel{0} \\
-\ 1\ 3\ 2 \\
\hline
0\ 4\ 8
\end{array}
$$

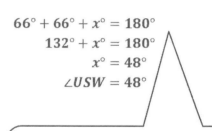

$$66° + 66° + x° = 180°$$
$$132° + x° = 180°$$
$$x° = 48°$$
$$∠USW = 48°$$

I know a straight angle measures 180°.
I subtract 112° from 180° to find the value of $x°$.
To verify my answer, I use my protractor to measure the angle. It measures 68°.

I know that the sum of these three angle measures is 180°. I add the two parts that I know and then I subtract their total from 180°.

2. Complete the following directions in the space to the right.

   a. Draw 2 points: S and T. Using a straightedge, draw $\overleftrightarrow{ST}$.

   b. Plot a point U somewhere between points S and T.

   c. Plot a point W, which is not on $\overleftrightarrow{ST}$.

   d. Draw $\overline{UW}$.

   e. Find the measure of ∠SUW and ∠TUW.

   f. Write an equation to show that the angles add to the measure of a straight angle.

   Sample Response:

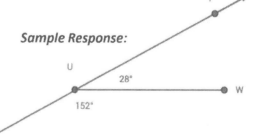

I draw the figure. I use my protractor to measure ∠SUW and ∠TUW.

$$∠SUW = 152°$$

$$∠TUW = 28°$$

$$152° + 28° = 180°$$

Lesson 10: Use the addition of adjacent angle measures to solve problems using a symbol for the unknown angle measure.   **13**

©2015 Great Minds. eureka-math.org
G4-M1-HWH-1.3.0-07.2015

G4-M4-Lesson 11

Write an equation, and solve for the unknown angle measurements numerically.

1.

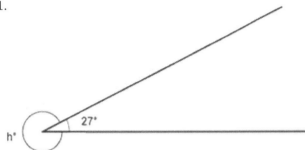

> I know from Lesson 5 that a circle measures 360°.
> I solve for $h°$ by subtracting 27° from 360°.

$$\underline{\quad 27°\quad} + \underline{\quad 333°\quad} = 360°$$

$$h° = \underline{\quad 333°\quad}$$

$$
\begin{array}{ccc}
 & 5 & 10 \\
3 & \cancel{6} & \cancel{0} \\
- & 2 & 7 \\
\hline
3 & 3 & 3 \\
\end{array}
$$

2.

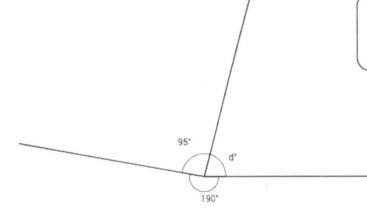

> I solve for $d°$ by adding together the known angle measures and then subtracting their sum from 360°.

$$\underline{\quad 190°\quad} + \underline{\quad 95°\quad} + \underline{\quad 75°\quad} = \underline{\quad 360°\quad}$$

$$d° = \underline{\quad 75°\quad}$$

$$
\begin{array}{crrr}
 & 1 & 9 & 0 \\
+ & & 9 & 5 \\
\hline
 & 2 & 8 & 5 \\
\end{array}
\qquad
\begin{array}{crrr}
 & & 15 & \\
 & 2 & \cancel{5} & 10 \\
 & \cancel{3} & \cancel{6} & \cancel{0} \\
- & 2 & 8 & 5 \\
\hline
 & & 7 & 5 \\
\end{array}
$$

14   Lesson 11:   Use the addition of adjacent angle measures to solve problems using a
                            symbol for the unknown angle measure.

©2015 Great Minds. eureka-math.org
G4-M1-HWH-1.3.0-07.2015

EUREKA MATH™

3. T is the intersection of $\overline{UV}$ and $\overline{WX}$. $g° = \underline{\ 129° \ }$ $h° = \underline{\ 51° \ }$ $i° = \underline{\ 129° \ }$
   $\angle UTW$ is 51°.

$$129° + h° = 180° \qquad 51° + i° = 180°$$
$$h° = 51° \qquad\qquad i° = 129°$$

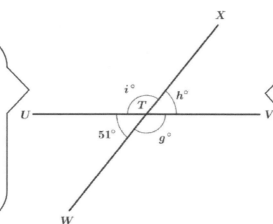

I can solve for $i°$ by thinking of its relationship to either $\overline{UV}$ or $\overline{WX}$. But I also notice that opposite angles measure the same for this figure.

I solve for $h°$ by thinking about the relationships of $\angle WTV$ and $\angle VTX$. Both angle measures add to 180° because they are on $\overline{WX}$.

$$51° + g° = 180°$$
$$g° = 129°$$

I solve for $g°$ by thinking of its relationship to $\angle UTW$. $\angle UTV$ is a straight angle that measures 180°.

$$
\begin{array}{r}
 & 7 & 10 \\
1 & \cancel{8} & \cancel{0} \\
- \quad & 5 & 1 \\
\hline
1 & 2 & 9 \\
\end{array}
$$

EUREKA MATH   **Lesson 11:**   Use the addition of adjacent angle measures to solve problems using a symbol for the unknown angle measure.   15

©2015 Great Minds. eureka-math.org
G4-M1-HWH-1.3.0-07.2015

4. P is the intersection of $\overline{QR}$, $\overline{ST}$, and $\overline{UP}$. $j° = \underline{\ 124°\ }$ $k° = \underline{\ 56°\ }$ $m° = \underline{\ 34°\ }$
    $\angle QPS$ is 56°.

$$
\begin{array}{r}
{\scriptstyle 7 \ \ 10} \\
1 \ \cancel{8} \ \cancel{0} \\
- \quad 5 \ \ 6 \\
\hline
1 \ \ 2 \ \ 4
\end{array}
$$

$56° + j° = 180°$
$\qquad j° = 124°$

$124° + k° = 180°$
$\qquad k° = 56°$

$$
\begin{array}{r}
{\scriptstyle 7 \ \ 10} \\
1 \ \cancel{8} \ \cancel{0} \\
- \quad 1 \ \ 2 \ \ 4 \\
\hline
0 \ \ 5 \ \ 6
\end{array}
$$

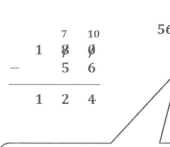

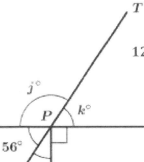

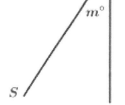

I solve for $j°$ by thinking of the relationship $\angle SPQ$ and $\angle QPT$ have to $\overline{ST}$.

I solve for $k°$ by thinking of the relationship $\angle QPT$ and $\angle TPR$ have to $\overline{QR}$.

I solve for $m°$ by noticing that $\angle UPR$ is a right angle; therefore, $\angle UPQ$ is also a right angle.

$56° + m° = 90°$
$\qquad m° = 34°$

$$
\begin{array}{r}
{\scriptstyle 8 \ \ 10} \\
\cancel{9} \ \cancel{0} \\
- \quad 5 \ \ 6 \\
\hline
3 \ \ 4
\end{array}
$$

Lesson 11:   Use the addition of adjacent angle measures to solve problems using a
                          symbol for the unknown angle measure.

©2015 Great Minds. eureka-math.org
G4-M1-HWH-1.3.0-07.2015

G4-M4-Lesson 12

> I can tell parts (b) and (d) each have a line of symmetry because the figure in each part is the same on both sides of the line.

1. Circle the figures that have a correct line of symmetry drawn.

   a.   b.   c.   d.

   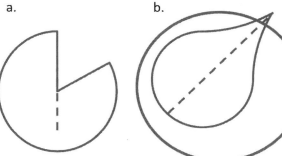
   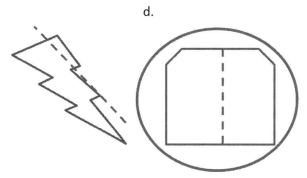

2. Find and draw all lines of symmetry for the following figures. Write the number of lines of symmetry that you found in the blank underneath the shape.

   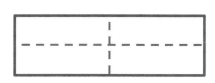
   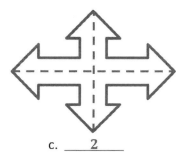

   a. ___1___   b. ___2___   c. ___2___

   > I think about folding these shapes in half many different ways. If the shapes match where I fold them, that is a line of symmetry.

EUREKA
MATH™

Lesson 12:   Recognize lines of symmetry for given two-dimensional figures. Identify line-symmetric figures, and draw lines of symmetry.   **17**

©2015 Great Minds. eureka-math.org
G4-M1-HWH-1.3.0-07.2015

3. Half of the figure below has been drawn. Use the line of symmetry, represented by the dashed line, to complete the figure.

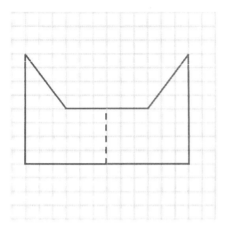

I use the grid to help me complete the figure. I count how many units long each segment is, and then I draw segments of the same length for the other half of the figure. I draw the sides that follow the grid lines first, and then I make the diagonal line.

G4-M4-Lesson 13

1. Classify each triangle by its side lengths and angle measurements. Circle the correct names.

		Classify Using Side Lengths	Classify Using Angle Measurements
a.		Equilateral Isosceles (Scalene)	Acute (Right) Obtuse
b.		Equilateral (Isosceles) Scalene	Acute Right (Obtuse)
c.		(Equilateral) Isosceles Scalene	(Acute) Right Obtuse

Sometimes triangles are drawn with tick marks, little dashes perpendicular to the sides of the triangle. These tick marks mean that those sides have the same length.

To classify by side lengths, I use a ruler to measure each side of the triangle or look to see if tick marks are drawn. Equilateral triangles have sides that are all the same length. Isosceles triangles have two sides that are the same length. Scalene triangles have sides that are all different lengths.

To classify by angle measure, I can use a protractor or a right angle template. An acute triangle has three angles less than 90°.

A right triangle has one 90° angle. An obtuse triangle has one angle greater than 90°.

2. Use a ruler to connect points to form two other triangles. Use each point only once. None of the triangles may overlap. One point will be unused. Name and classify the three triangles below. The first one has been done for you.

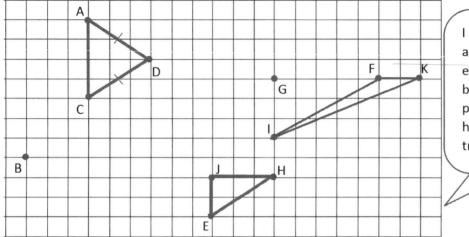

I draw two triangles and then classify each of them. I look back to the first problem to recall how to classify the triangles.

Name the Triangles Using Vertices	Classify by Side Length	Classify by Angle Measurement
△ FKI	Scalene	Obtuse
△ ACD	Isosceles	Acute
△ EHJ	Scalene	Right

3. Can a triangle have two obtuse angles? Explain.

Sample answer:

No, if a triangle had two obtuse angles, the three sides could never meet.

I draw two obtuse angles, and I see that the three sides can't form a triangle since two of the line segments will continue to get farther apart instead of closer together if I make them longer.

Lesson 13:   Analyze and classify triangles based on side length, angle measure, or both.

EUREKA
MATH™

G4-M4-Lesson 14

1. Draw triangles that fit the following classifications. Use a ruler and protractor. Label the side lengths and angles.

   a.   Acute and equilateral

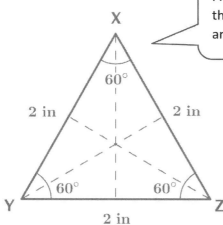

   I remember from Lesson 9 that an equilateral triangle has angle measurements of 60°.

   To draw this triangle, I first use my protractor to draw the right angle. Then I use my ruler to make sure $\overline{EG}$ and $\overline{GF}$ are the same length.

   b.   Right and isosceles

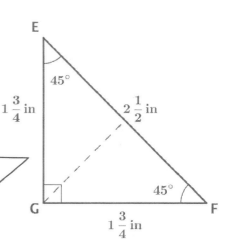

2. Draw all possible lines of symmetry in the triangles above.

   △ XYZ has three lines of symmetry because it is an equilateral triangle.
   △ EFG has one line of symmetry because it is an isosceles triangle.

3. △ EFG can be described as a right triangle and a scalene triangle. True or False?

   Sample answer:

   False. △ EFG is isosceles and right. I know this because two of the sides are the same length, and there is a right angle.

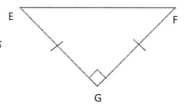

EUREKA MATH   **Lesson 14:**   Define and construct triangles from given criteria. Explore symmetry in triangles.   **21**

©2015 Great Minds. eureka-math.org
G4-M1-HWH-1.3.0-07.2015

4. If △ ABC is an equilateral triangle, $\overline{BC}$ must be 1 cm. True or False?

Sample answer:

True. If △ ABC is equilateral, that means that all of the side lengths must be the same length. So, if two of the sides are 1 cm, the third side must also be 1 cm.

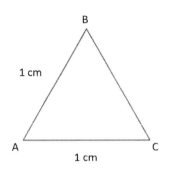

Lesson 14: Define and construct triangles from given criteria. Explore symmetry in triangles.

©2015 Great Minds. eureka-math.org
G4-M1-HWH-1.3.0-07.2015

G4-M4-Lesson 15

> I use what I learned in Lessons 3 and 4 to draw parallel and perpendicular lines using a right angle template and a ruler.

Construct the following figures based on the given attributes. Give a name to each figure you construct. Be as specific as possible.

1. A quadrilateral with opposite sides the same length and four right angles

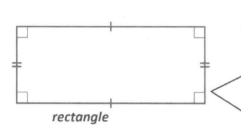

rectangle

> I draw the bottom segment using my ruler. I draw the two sides using my right angle template and ruler to make right angles and to make the left and right side lengths equal. I draw the top segment perpendicular to the sides and parallel to the bottom segment. I draw small squares to show the right angles and tick marks to show which sides are equal.

2. A quadrilateral with one set of parallel sides

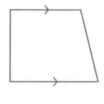

trapezoid

> I draw a horizontal segment. I draw a segment that is parallel to the first segment. I connect the endpoints of the segments. I draw arrows to label the parallel sides.

3. A quadrilateral with two sets of parallel sides

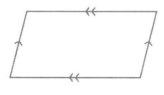

parallelogram

> I start by drawing horizontal, parallel sides just as when I started drawing a trapezoid. After I draw the left side segment, I make sure the right side segment is parallel to it. I add arrows on the opposite segments to show they are parallel to each other.

©2015 Great Minds. eureka-math.org
G4-M1-HWH-1.3.0-07.2015

4. A parallelogram with all sides the same length and four right angles

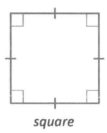

square

I start by drawing a parallelogram, except I draw the left side segment perpendicular to the horizontal segments. I measure the left side segment and make sure to make the top and bottom segments the same lengths. I draw a right segment perpendicular to the top and bottom segments. It will be the same length as all other sides. I add tick marks and right angle squares.

©2015 Great Minds. eureka-math.org
G4-M1-HWH-1.3.0-07.2015

G4-M4-Lesson 16

1. Construct a quadrilateral with all sides of equal length. What shape did you create?

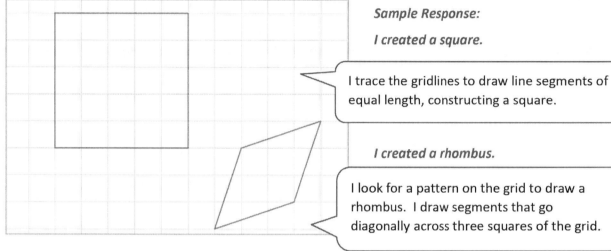

Sample Response:

I created a square.

> I trace the gridlines to draw line segments of equal length, constructing a square.

I created a rhombus.

> I look for a pattern on the grid to draw a rhombus. I draw segments that go diagonally across three squares of the grid.

2. Construct a quadrilateral with two sets of parallel sides. What shape did you create?

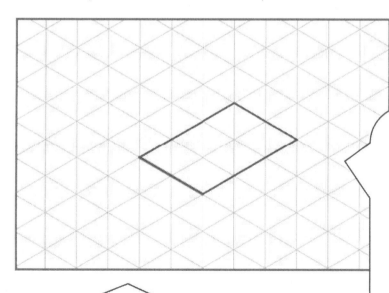

Sample Response:

I created a parallelogram.

> I trace along one of the diagonal gridlines. I draw a second segment parallel to the first by tracing along a gridline two triangle side lengths away. I draw the third and fourth segments by tracing along two other diagonal gridlines going in the opposite direction. I use a ruler and right angle template to verify that the sets of sides are parallel.

> I also could have drawn a rectangle, a square, or a rhombus because they are also quadrilaterals with two sets of parallel sides.

©2015 Great Minds. eureka-math.org
G4-M1-HWH-1.3.0-07.2015

Homework Helpers

Grade 4
Module 5

G4-M5-Lesson 1

1. Draw a number bond, and write the number sentence to match each tape diagram.

a.

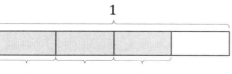

> The rectangle represents 1 and is partitioned into 4 equal units. Each unit is equal to 1 fourth.

$$\frac{3}{4} = \frac{1}{4} + \frac{1}{4} + \frac{1}{4}$$

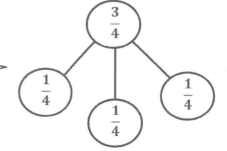

> I can decompose any fraction into unit fractions. 3 fourths is composed of 3 units of 1 fourth.

b.

> I can rename a fraction greater than 1, such as $\frac{10}{8}$, as a whole number and a fraction, $1\frac{2}{8}$.

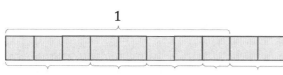

$$\frac{10}{8} = \frac{3}{8} + \frac{2}{8} + \frac{2}{8} + \frac{1}{8} + \frac{2}{8}$$

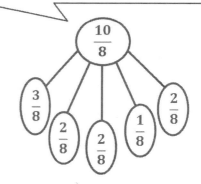

> I know the fractional unit is eighths. I count 8 equal units bracketed as 1 whole.

2. Draw and label tape diagrams to match each number sentence.

a. $\frac{11}{6} = \frac{3}{6} + \frac{2}{6} + \frac{2}{6} + \frac{4}{6}$

b. $1\frac{2}{12} = \frac{7}{12} + \frac{4}{12} + \frac{3}{12}$

> I know the unit is twelfths. I partition my tape diagram into 12 equal units to represent the whole. I draw 2 more twelfths.

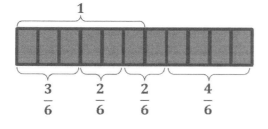

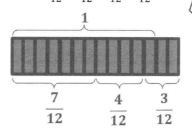

EUREKA MATH

Lesson 1:   Decompose fractions as a sum of unit fractions using tape diagrams.

1

©2015 Great Minds. eureka-math.org
G4-M1-HWH-1.3.0-07.2015

G4-M5-Lesson 2

Step 1: Draw and shade a tape diagram of the given fraction.

Step 2: Record the decomposition as a sum of unit fractions.

Step 3: Record the decomposition of the fraction two more ways.

1. $\frac{4}{8}$

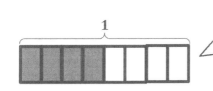

The bottom number in the fraction determines the fractional size. I draw a whole partitioned into 8 equal parts.

$$\frac{4}{8} = \frac{1}{8} + \frac{1}{8} + \frac{1}{8} + \frac{1}{8}$$

$\frac{1}{8}$ is a unit fraction because it identifies 1 of the specified fractional size, eighths.

Sample Student Responses:

$$\frac{4}{8} = \frac{2}{8} + \frac{1}{8} + \frac{1}{8}$$

$$\frac{4}{8} = \frac{3}{8} + \frac{1}{8}$$

Adding fractions is like adding whole numbers. Just as 3 ones plus 1 one is 4 ones, 3 eighths plus 1 eighth is 4 eighths.

Step 1: Draw and shade a tape diagram of the given fraction.

Step 2: Record the decomposition of the fraction in three different ways using number sentences.

2. $\frac{8}{5}$

This fraction is greater than 1.

5 fifths is equal to 1.

Sample Student Responses:

$$\frac{8}{5} = 1 + \frac{3}{5}$$

$$\frac{8}{5} = \frac{4}{5} + \frac{4}{5}$$

$$\frac{8}{5} = \frac{2}{5} + \frac{2}{5} + \frac{3}{5} + \frac{1}{5}$$

G4-M5-Lesson 3

1. Decompose each fraction modeled by a tape diagram as a sum of unit fractions. Write the equivalent multiplication sentence.

   a.   1

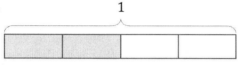

$$\frac{2}{4} = \frac{1}{4} + \frac{1}{4}$$ $$\frac{2}{4} = 2 \times \frac{1}{4}$$ There are 2 copies of $\frac{1}{4}$ shaded, so I write $2 \times \frac{1}{4}$.

   I can multiply fourths like I multiply any other unit. 1 banana times 2 is 2 bananas and 1 ten times 2 is 2 tens, so 1 fourth times 2 is 2 fourths.

   b.   1

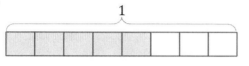

$$\frac{5}{8} = \frac{1}{8} + \frac{1}{8} + \frac{1}{8} + \frac{1}{8} + \frac{1}{8}$$ $$\frac{5}{8} = 5 \times \frac{1}{8}$$ I can add 1 eighth 5 times. Whew! That's a lot of writing! Or I can multiply to show 5 copies of $\frac{1}{8}$.

2. The tape diagram models a fraction greater than 1. Write the fraction greater than 1 as the sum of two products.

   This bracket identifies the whole. This tape diagram models a fraction greater than 1.

                      1

$$\frac{7}{5} = \left(5 \times \frac{1}{5}\right) + \left(2 \times \frac{1}{5}\right)$$

   I see in the tape diagram that $\frac{7}{5}$ is the same as $1\frac{2}{5}$. I can use the distributive property to express the whole part and the fractional part as 2 different multiplication expressions.

3. Draw a tape diagram to model $\frac{9}{8}$. Record the decomposition of $\frac{9}{8}$ into unit fractions as a multiplication sentence.

                      1

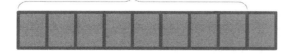

$$\frac{9}{8} = 9 \times \frac{1}{8}$$

EUREKA MATH   **Lesson 3:**   Decompose non-unit fractions and represent them as a whole number times a unit fraction using tape diagrams.   3

©2015 Great Minds. eureka-math.org
G4-M1-HWH-1.3.0-07.2015

G4-M5-Lesson 4

1. The total length of each tape diagram represents 1. Decompose the shaded unit fractions as the sum of smaller unit fractions in at least two different ways.

a.

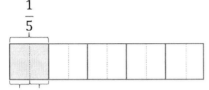

$\frac{1}{5} = \frac{1}{10} + \frac{1}{10}$

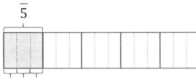

$\frac{1}{15} + \frac{1}{15} + \frac{1}{15} = \frac{1}{5}$

After decomposing each fifth into 2 equal parts, the new unit is tenths.

b.

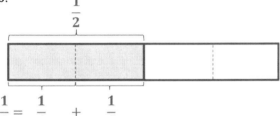

$\frac{1}{2} = \frac{1}{4} + \frac{1}{4}$

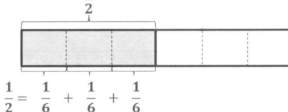

$\frac{1}{2} = \frac{1}{6} + \frac{1}{6} + \frac{1}{6}$

2. Draw a tape diagram to prove $\frac{2}{3} = \frac{4}{6}$.

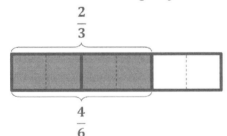

I know that $\frac{2}{3}$ and $\frac{4}{6}$ are equal because they take up the same amount of space.

3. Show that $\frac{1}{2}$ is equivalent to $\frac{4}{8}$ using a tape diagram and a number sentence.

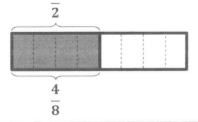

$\frac{1}{2} = 4 \times \frac{1}{8}$

I quadrupled the number of units within each half, which I can record as a multiplication sentence.

Lesson 4:   Decompose fractions into sums of smaller unit fractions using tape
                           diagrams.

G4-M5-Lesson 5

1. Draw horizontal line(s) to decompose the rectangle into 2 rows. Use the model to name the shaded area as both a sum of unit fractions and as a multiplication sentence.

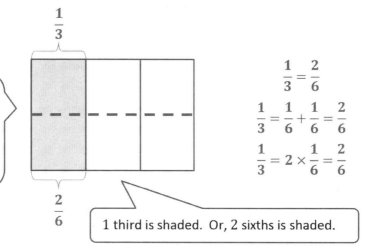

$\frac{1}{3}$

I draw 1 horizontal line to decompose the whole into 2 equal rows. Now there are 6 equal units in all. 2 sixths is the same as 1 third.

$\frac{2}{6}$

1 third is shaded. Or, 2 sixths is shaded.

$$\frac{1}{3} = \frac{2}{6}$$

$$\frac{1}{3} = \frac{1}{6} + \frac{1}{6} = \frac{2}{6}$$

$$\frac{1}{3} = 2 \times \frac{1}{6} = \frac{2}{6}$$

2. Draw area models to show the decompositions represented by the number sentences below. Represent the decomposition as a sum of unit fractions and as a multiplication sentence.

a. $\frac{1}{2} = \frac{2}{4}$

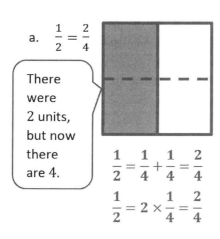

There were 2 units, but now there are 4.

$$\frac{1}{2} = \frac{1}{4} + \frac{1}{4} = \frac{2}{4}$$

$$\frac{1}{2} = 2 \times \frac{1}{4} = \frac{2}{4}$$

b. $\frac{1}{2} = \frac{6}{12}$

After decomposing, there are *more* units, and they are *smaller*.

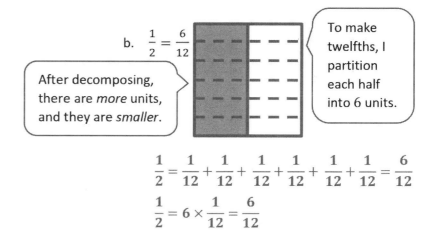

To make twelfths, I partition each half into 6 units.

$$\frac{1}{2} = \frac{1}{12} + \frac{1}{12} + \frac{1}{12} + \frac{1}{12} + \frac{1}{12} + \frac{1}{12} = \frac{6}{12}$$

$$\frac{1}{2} = 6 \times \frac{1}{12} = \frac{6}{12}$$

3. Explain why $\frac{1}{12} + \frac{1}{12} + \frac{1}{12} + \frac{1}{12} + \frac{1}{12} + \frac{1}{12}$ is the same as $\frac{1}{2}$.

Sample Student Response:

I see in the area model that I drew that 6 twelfths takes up the same space as 1 half. 6 twelfths and 1 half have exactly the same area.

G4-M5-Lesson 6

1. The rectangle represents 1. Draw horizontal line(s) to decompose the rectangle into *twelfths*. Use the model to name the shaded area as a sum and as a product of unit fractions. Use parentheses to show the relationship between the number sentences.

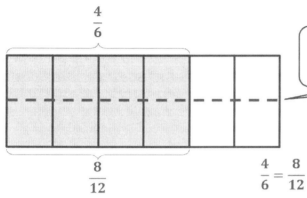

$\dfrac{4}{6}$

$\dfrac{8}{12}$

4 sixths are shaded. I draw one line to partition sixths into twelfths. 8 twelfths are shaded.

$\dfrac{4}{6} = \dfrac{8}{12}$

I write addition and multiplication sentences using unit fractions.

$$\frac{1}{6} + \frac{1}{6} + \frac{1}{6} + \frac{1}{6} = \left(\frac{1}{12} + \frac{1}{12}\right) + \left(\frac{1}{12} + \frac{1}{12}\right) + \left(\frac{1}{12} + \frac{1}{12}\right) + \left(\frac{1}{12} + \frac{1}{12}\right) = \frac{8}{12}$$

$$\left(\frac{1}{12} + \frac{1}{12}\right) + \left(\frac{1}{12} + \frac{1}{12}\right) + \left(\frac{1}{12} + \frac{1}{12}\right) + \left(\frac{1}{12} + \frac{1}{12}\right) = \left(2 \times \frac{1}{12}\right) + \left(2 \times \frac{1}{12}\right) + \left(2 \times \frac{1}{12}\right) + \left(2 \times \frac{1}{12}\right) = \frac{8}{12}$$

$$\frac{4}{6} = 8 \times \frac{1}{12} = \frac{8}{12}$$

2. Draw an area model to show the decompositions represented by $\dfrac{2}{3} = \dfrac{6}{9}$. Express $\dfrac{2}{3} = \dfrac{6}{9}$ as a sum and product of unit fractions. Use parentheses to show the relationship between the number sentences.

$\dfrac{2}{3}$

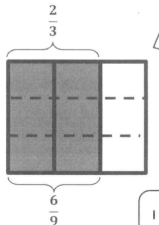

$\dfrac{6}{9}$

I draw thirds vertically and partition the thirds into ninths with two horizontal lines.

$$\frac{2}{3} = \frac{6}{9}$$

$$\frac{1}{3} + \frac{1}{3} = \left(\frac{1}{9} + \frac{1}{9} + \frac{1}{9}\right) + \left(\frac{1}{9} + \frac{1}{9} + \frac{1}{9}\right) = \frac{6}{9}$$

$$\left(\frac{1}{9} + \frac{1}{9} + \frac{1}{9}\right) + \left(\frac{1}{9} + \frac{1}{9} + \frac{1}{9}\right) = \left(3 \times \frac{1}{9}\right) + \left(3 \times \frac{1}{9}\right) = \frac{6}{9}$$

I write parentheses that show the decomposition of $\dfrac{1}{3}$. Just as the area model shows 1 third partitioned into 3 ninths, so do the parentheses.

EUREKA MATH™

G4-M5-Lesson 7

Each rectangle represents 1.

1. The shaded unit fractions have been decomposed into smaller units. Express the equivalent fractions in a number sentence using multiplication.

   a.

   $$\frac{1}{3} = \frac{1 \times 2}{3 \times 2} = \frac{2}{6}$$

   b.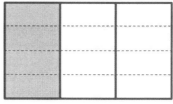

   $$\frac{1}{3} = \frac{1 \times 4}{3 \times 4} = \frac{4}{12}$$

   > The numerator is 1.
   > The denominator is 3.

   > I can multiply the numerator (number of fractional units selected) and the denominator (the fractional unit) by 4 to make an equivalent fraction.

2. Decompose the shaded fraction into smaller units using the area model. Express the equivalent fractions in a number sentence using multiplication.

   > The area model shows that $\frac{1}{6}$ equals $\frac{3}{18}$.

   > As I multiply, the size of the units gets smaller.

   $$\frac{1}{6} = \frac{1 \times 3}{6 \times 3} = \frac{3}{18}$$

3. Draw three different area models to represent 1 half by shading.

   Decompose the shaded fraction into (a) fourths, (b) sixths, and (c) eighths.

   Use multiplication to show how each fraction is equivalent to 1 half.

   a.

   $$\frac{1}{2} = \frac{1 \times 2}{2 \times 2} = \frac{2}{4}$$

   > The number of units doubled.

   b.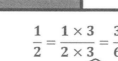

   $$\frac{1}{2} = \frac{1 \times 3}{2 \times 3} = \frac{3}{6}$$

   > The number of units tripled.

   c.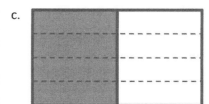

   $$\frac{1}{2} = \frac{1 \times 4}{2 \times 4} = \frac{4}{8}$$

   > The number of units quadrupled.

G4-M5-Lesson 8

Each rectangle represents 1.

1. The shaded fraction has been decomposed into smaller units. Express the equivalent fraction in a number sentence using multiplication.

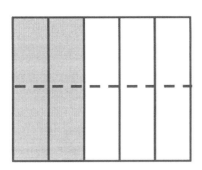

$$\frac{2}{5} = \frac{2 \times 2}{5 \times 2} = \frac{4}{10}$$

> The number of units in the area model has been doubled. There were 5 units, and now there are 10 units.

2. Decompose both shaded fractions into sixteenths. Express the equivalent fractions in a number sentence using multiplication.

a.

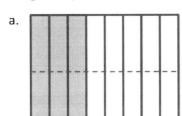

$$\frac{3}{8} = \frac{3 \times 2}{8 \times 2} = \frac{6}{16}$$

> I draw 1 line to partition each unit into 2.

b.

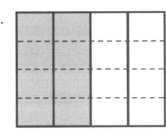

$$\frac{2}{4} = \frac{2 \times 4}{4 \times 4} = \frac{8}{16}$$

> I draw 3 lines to partition each unit into 4.

3. Use multiplication to create an equivalent fraction for the fraction $\frac{8}{6}$.

$$\frac{8}{6} = \frac{8 \times 2}{6 \times 2} = \frac{16}{12}$$

> To make an equivalent fraction, I can choose any fraction equivalent to 1. I can choose $\frac{3}{3}, \frac{4}{4}, \frac{5}{5}$, etc.

4. Determine if the following is a true number sentence. Correct it if it is false by changing the right-hand side of the number sentence.

$$\frac{5}{4} = \frac{15}{16}$$

Sample Student Response:

Not true!

$$\frac{5}{4} = \frac{5 \times 3}{4 \times 3} = \frac{15}{12}$$

> This is false! The numerator was multiplied by 3. The denominator was multiplied by 4. Three fourths is not a fraction equal to 1.

Lesson 8:   Use the area model and multiplication to show the equivalence of two fractions.

G4-M5-Lesson 9

Each rectangle represents 1.

1. Compose the shaded fraction into larger fractional units. Express the equivalent fractions in a number sentence using division.

   a.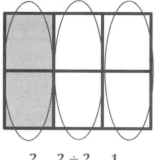

    2 units are shaded. I make groups of 2. Sixths are composed as thirds.

   b.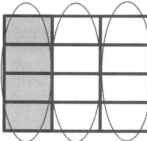

   $$\frac{2}{6} = \frac{2 \div 2}{6 \div 2} = \frac{1}{3}$$

   I divide the numerator and denominator by 2.

   $$\frac{4}{12} = \frac{4 \div 4}{12 \div 4} = \frac{1}{3}$$

   When I compose thirds, the number of units decreases. I make a larger unit.

2.

   a. In the first model, show 2 tenths. In the second area model, show 3 fifteenths. Show how both fractions can be composed, or renamed, as the same unit fraction.

   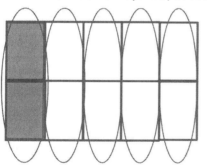   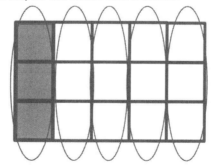

   Before I draw my model, I identify the larger unit fraction. I know 3 fifteenths is the same as $\frac{1 \times 3}{5 \times 3}$.

   2 tenths = 1 fifth   *3 fifteenths = 1 fifth*

b. Express the equivalent fractions in a number sentence using division.

$$\frac{2}{10} = \frac{2 \div 2}{10 \div 2} = \frac{1}{5}$$ $$\frac{3}{15} = \frac{3 \div 3}{15 \div 3} = \frac{1}{5}$$

I circled groups of 2 units, so I divide the numerator and denominator by 2.   I circled groups of 3 units, so I divide the numerator and denominator by 3.

Lesson 9:   Use the area model and division to show the equivalence of two fractions.

EUREKA MATH

G4-M5-Lesson 10

Each rectangle represents 1.

1. Compose the shaded fraction into larger fractional units. Express the equivalent fractions in a number sentence using division.

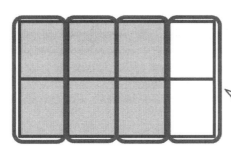

$$\frac{6}{8} = \frac{6 \div 2}{8 \div 2} = \frac{3}{4}$$

> This work is a lot like what I did in Lesson 9. However, once I compose units, the renamed fraction is not a unit fraction.

2. Draw an area model to represent the number sentence below.

$$\frac{4}{14} = \frac{4 \div 2}{14 \div 2} = \frac{2}{7}$$

> Looking at the numerator and denominator, I draw 14 units and shade 4 units.

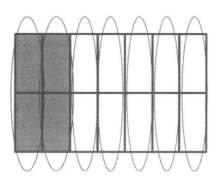

> Looking at the divisor, $\frac{2}{2}$, I circle groups of 2. I make 7 groups. 2 sevenths are shaded.

3. Use division to rename the fraction below. Draw a model if that helps you. See if you can use the largest common factor.

$$\frac{8}{20} = \frac{8 \div 4}{20 \div 4} = \frac{2}{5}$$

> I could choose 2, but the largest common factor is 4.

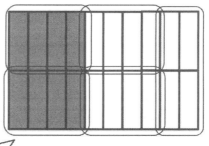

> Whether I compose units vertically or horizontally, I get the same answer!

EUREKA
MATH™

Lesson 10:   Use the area model and division to show the equivalence of two
fractions.

11

©2015 Great Minds. eureka-math.org
G4-M1-HWH-1.3.0-07.2015

G4-M5-Lesson 11

1. Label each number line with the fractions shown on the tape diagram. Circle the fraction that labels the point on the number line and also names the shaded part of the tape diagram.

   a.

   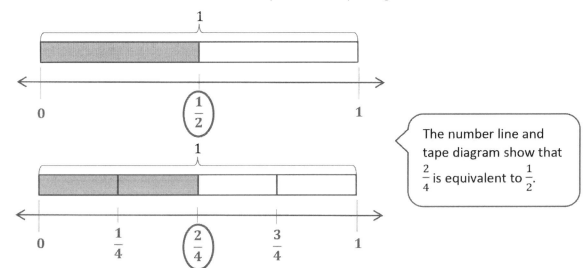

   b.

   The number line and tape diagram show that $\frac{2}{4}$ is equivalent to $\frac{1}{2}$.

2. Write number sentences using multiplication to show the fraction represented in 1(a) is equivalent to the fraction represented in 1(b).

$$\frac{1}{2} = \frac{1 \times 2}{2 \times 2} = \frac{2}{4}$$

3.

   a. Partition a number line from 0 to 1 into thirds. Decompose $\frac{2}{3}$ into 4 equal lengths.

   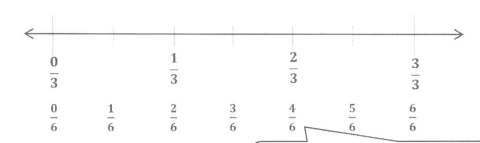

   To decompose 2 thirds into 4 equal parts, each unit is partitioned into two. To name the new, smaller units, I decompose each third. Thirds become sixths, so $\frac{2}{3} = \frac{4}{6}$.

Lesson 11:   Explain fraction equivalence using a tape diagram and the number line, and relate that to the use of multiplication and division.

©2015 Great Minds. eureka-math.org
G4-M1-HWH-1.3.0-07.2015

EUREKA
MATH™

©2015 Great Minds. eureka-math.org
G4-M1-HWH-1.3.0-07.2015

b. Write 1 multiplication and 1 division sentence to show what fraction represented on the number line is equivalent to $\frac{2}{3}$.

$$\frac{2}{3} = \frac{2 \times 2}{3 \times 2} = \frac{4}{6}$$

$$\frac{4}{6} = \frac{4 \div 2}{6 \div 2} = \frac{2}{3}$$

EUREKA MATH

Lesson 11: Explain fraction equivalence using a tape diagram and the number line, and relate that to the use of multiplication and division.

13

G4-M5-Lesson 12

1.

a.   Plot the following points on the number line without measuring.

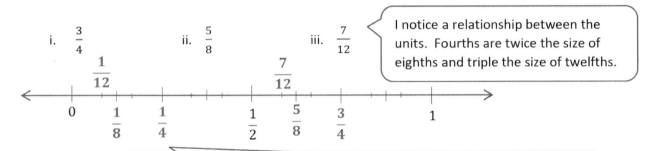

i. $\frac{3}{4}$ ii. $\frac{5}{8}$ iii. $\frac{7}{12}$

> I notice a relationship between the units. Fourths are twice the size of eighths and triple the size of twelfths.

> I use benchmark fractions I know to plot twelfths. After marking fourths, I know that 1 fourth is the same as 3 twelfths, so I decompose each fourth into 3 units to make twelfths.

b.   Use the number line in part (a) to compare the fractions by writing >, <, or = on the lines.

i. $\frac{3}{4}$ __>__ $\frac{1}{2}$ ii. $\frac{7}{12}$ __<__ $\frac{5}{8}$

c.   Explain how you plotted the points in Part (a).

Sample Student Response:

The number line was partitioned into halves. I doubled the units to make fourths. I plotted 3 fourths. I doubled the units again to make eighths. Knowing that 1 half and 4 eighths are equivalent fractions, I simply counted on 1 more eighth to plot 5 eighths. Lastly, I thought about twelfths and fourths. 1 fourth is the same as 3 twelfths. I marked twelfths by partitioning each fourth into 3 units. I plotted 7 twelfths.

EUREKA MATH

©2015 Great Minds. eureka-math.org
G4-M1-HWH-1.3.0-07.2015

2. Compare the fractions given below by writing < or > on the line.

    Give a brief explanation for each answer referring to the benchmarks of $0, \frac{1}{2}$, and/or 1.

    $\frac{5}{8}$ ___>___ $\frac{6}{10}$

    Possible student response:

    If I think about eighths, I know that 1 half is equal to 4 eighths. Therefore, 5 eighths is 1 eighth greater than 1 half.

    I also know that 5 tenths is equal to 1 half. 6 tenths is 1 tenth greater than 1 half. Comparing the size of the units, I know that 1 eighth is more than 1 tenth. So, 5 eighths is greater than 6 tenths.

Lesson 12:   Reason using benchmarks to compare two fractions on the number line.   15

G4-M5-Lesson 13

1. Place the following fractions on the number line given.

$\frac{8}{4}$ is equal to 2. Therefore, $\frac{7}{4}$ is 1 fourth less than 2.

a. $\frac{7}{4}$ b. $\frac{3}{2}$ c. $\frac{11}{8}$

I can draw a number bond, breaking $\frac{11}{8}$ into $\frac{8}{8}$ and $\frac{3}{8}$.

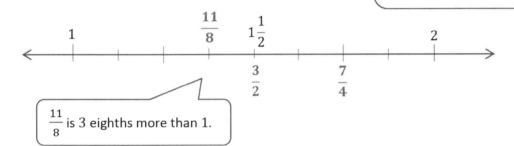

$\frac{11}{8}$ is 3 eighths more than 1.

2. Use the number line in Problem 1 to compare the fractions by writing <, >, or = on the lines.

   a. $1\frac{3}{4}$ __>__ $1\frac{1}{2}$ b. $1\frac{3}{8}$ __<__ $1\frac{3}{4}$

Using the benchmark $\frac{1}{2}$, I compare the fractions. $1\frac{3}{8}$ is less than 1 and 1 half, while $1\frac{3}{4}$ is more than 1 and 1 half.

3. Use the number line in Problem 1 to explain the reasoning you used when determining whether $\frac{11}{8}$ or $\frac{7}{4}$ was greater.

   Sample Student Response:

   After I plotted $\frac{11}{8}$ and $\frac{7}{4}$, I noticed that $\frac{7}{4}$ was greater than $1\frac{1}{2}$, whereas $\frac{11}{8}$ is less than $1\frac{1}{2}$.

EUREKA
MATH™

4. Compare the fractions given below by writing $<$ or $>$ on the lines. Give a brief explanation for each answer referring to benchmarks.

a. $\dfrac{5}{4}$ ___ $>$ ___ $\dfrac{9}{10}$

$\dfrac{5}{4}$ *is greater than* 1.

$\dfrac{9}{10}$ *is less than* 1.

b. $\dfrac{7}{12}$ ___ $<$ ___ $\dfrac{7}{6}$

> I use two different benchmarks to compare these fractions.

$\dfrac{7}{12}$ *is one twelfth greater than* $\dfrac{1}{2}$.

$\dfrac{7}{6}$ *is one sixth greater than* 1.

©2015 Great Minds. eureka-math.org
G4-M1-HWH-1.3.0-07.2015

G4-M5-Lesson 14

1. Compare the pairs of fractions by reasoning about the size of the units. Use >, <, or =.

   a. 1 fourth ___>___ 1 eighth

   b. 2 thirds ___>___ 2 fifths

   > I envision a tape diagram. 1 fourth is double the size of 1 eighth.

   > When I'm comparing the same number of units, I consider the size of the fractional unit. Thirds are bigger than fifths.

2. Compare by reasoning about the following pair of fractions with related numerators. Use >, <, or =. Explain your thinking using words, pictures, or numbers.

   $\frac{3}{7}$ __>__ $\frac{6}{15}$

   > To compare, I can make the numerators the same.

   3 sevenths are equal to 6 fourteenths. Fourteenths are greater than fifteenths. So, 3 sevenths are greater than 6 fifteenths.

3. Draw two tape diagrams to model and compare $1\frac{3}{4}$ and $1\frac{8}{12}$.

   $1\frac{3}{4}$ __>__ $1\frac{8}{12}$

   > The model shows that $\frac{9}{12}$ is equal to $\frac{3}{4}$. So, $\frac{8}{12}$ is less.

   > I'm careful to make each tape diagram the same size.

   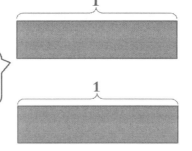
   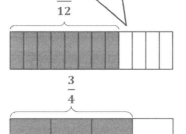

4. Draw one number line to model the pair of fractions with related denominators. Use >, <, or = to compare.

   $\frac{3}{12}$ __<__ $\frac{2}{6}$

EUREKA MATH™

G4-M5-Lesson 15

1. Draw an area model for the pair of fractions, and use it to compare the two fractions by writing $<$, $>$, or $=$ on the line.

$$\frac{4}{5} \ \underline{<} \ \frac{6}{7}$$

$$\frac{28}{35} \ \underline{<} \ \frac{30}{35}$$

$$\frac{4 \times 7}{5 \times 7} = \frac{28}{35}$$

> I use two area models that are exactly the same size to find like units. After partitioning, I have 35 units in each model. Now I can compare!

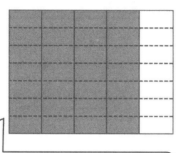

$$\frac{6 \times 5}{7 \times 5} = \frac{30}{35}$$

> I represent fifths with vertical lines and then partition fifths by drawing horizontal lines.

> I represent sevenths with horizontal lines and then partition sevenths by drawing vertical lines.

2. Rename the fractions below using multiplication, and then compare by writing $<$, $>$, or $=$.

$$\frac{5}{8} \ \underline{<} \ \frac{9}{12} \qquad \frac{5 \times 12}{8 \times 12} = \frac{60}{96} \qquad \frac{9 \times 8}{12 \times 8} = \frac{72}{96}$$

$$\frac{60}{96} \ \underline{<} \ \frac{72}{96}$$

> Whew! That would have been a lot of units to draw in an area model!

> Using multiplication to make common units is quick and precise. It is best to compare fractions when the units are the same.

3. Use any method to compare the fractions below. Record your answer using $<$, $>$, or $=$.

$$\frac{5}{3} \; \underline{<} \; \frac{9}{5}$$

$$\frac{3}{3} \; = \; \frac{5}{5}$$

$$\frac{2}{3} \; < \; \frac{4}{5}$$

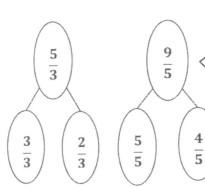

> I use benchmarks to compare. $\frac{4}{5}$ is closer to 1 than $\frac{2}{3}$ because fifths are smaller than thirds.

> I use number bonds to decompose fractions greater than 1. This lets me focus on the fractional parts, $\frac{2}{3}$ and $\frac{4}{5}$, to compare since $\frac{3}{3}$ and $\frac{5}{5}$ are equivalent.

EUREKA
MATH™

©2015 Great Minds. eureka-math.org
G4-M1-HWH-1.3.0-07.2015

G4-M5-Lesson 16

Solve.

1. 5 sixths − 3 sixths = ___2 *sixths*___

> The units in both numbers are the same, so I can think "5 − 3 = 2," so 5 sixths − 3 sixths = 2 sixths.

> I can rewrite the number sentence using fractions.
> $$\frac{5}{6} - \frac{3}{6} = \frac{2}{6}$$

2. 1 sixth + 4 sixths = ___5 *sixths*___

> If I know that 1 + 4 = 5, then 1 sixth + 4 sixths = 5 sixths.

Solve. Use a number bond to rename the sum or difference as a mixed number. Then, draw a number line to model your answer.

3. $\frac{12}{6} - \frac{5}{6} = \frac{7}{6} = 1\frac{1}{6}$

$\frac{6}{6}$ $\frac{1}{6}$

> I can rename $\frac{7}{6}$ as a mixed number using a number bond to separate, or decompose, $\frac{7}{6}$ into a whole number and a fraction. $\frac{6}{6}$ is the whole, and the fractional part is $\frac{1}{6}$.

4. $\frac{5}{6} + \frac{5}{6} = \frac{10}{6} = 1\frac{4}{6}$

$\frac{6}{6}$ $\frac{4}{6}$

> I decompose $\frac{10}{6}$ into 2 parts: $\frac{6}{6}$ and $\frac{4}{6}$. $\frac{6}{6}$ is the same as 1, so I rewrite $\frac{10}{6}$ as the mixed number $1\frac{4}{6}$.

> I can think of the number sentence in unit form: 5 sixths + 5 sixths = 10 sixths.

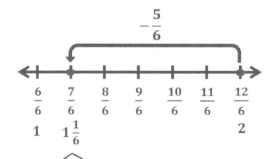

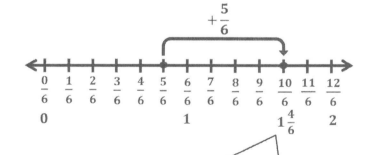

> I plot a point at $\frac{12}{6}$ because that is the whole. Then, I count backward to subtract $\frac{5}{6}$.

> I draw a number line and plot a point at $\frac{5}{6}$. I count up $\frac{5}{6}$. The model verifies the sum is $1\frac{4}{6}$.

G4-M5-Lesson 17

1. Use the three fractions $\frac{8}{8}$, $\frac{3}{8}$, and $\frac{5}{8}$ to write two addition and two subtraction number sentences.

$$\frac{3}{8} + \frac{5}{8} = \frac{8}{8} \qquad \frac{8}{8} - \frac{5}{8} = \frac{3}{8}$$

$$\frac{5}{8} + \frac{3}{8} = \frac{8}{8} \qquad \frac{8}{8} - \frac{3}{8} = \frac{5}{8}$$

> This is like the relationship between 3, 5, and 8:
>
> $$3 + 5 = 8 \qquad 8 - 5 = 3$$
> $$5 + 3 = 8 \qquad 8 - 3 = 5$$
>
> except these fractions have units of eighths.

2. Solve by subtracting and counting up. Model with a number line.

$$1 - \frac{3}{8}$$

$$\frac{8}{8} - \frac{3}{8} = \frac{5}{8}$$

> Or, I count up by thinking about how many eighths it takes to get from $\frac{3}{8}$ to $\frac{8}{8}$.
>
> $$\frac{3}{8} + x = \frac{8}{8}$$
> $$x = \frac{5}{8}$$

> I rename 1 as $\frac{8}{8}$. Now, I have like units, eighths, and I can subtract.

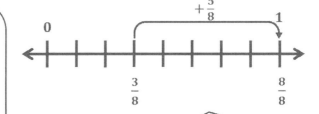

> A number line shows how to count up from $\frac{3}{8}$ to $\frac{8}{8}$. I can also start at 1 and show the subtraction of $\frac{3}{8}$ on the number line.

EUREKA MATH

3. Find the difference in two ways. Use a number bond to decompose the whole.

$$1\frac{5}{8} - \frac{7}{8}$$

$$\frac{8}{8} \qquad \frac{5}{8}$$

> I can use a number bond to rename $1\frac{5}{8}$ as $\frac{8}{8}$ and $\frac{5}{8}$.

$$\frac{8}{8} + \frac{5}{8} = \frac{13}{8}$$

$$\frac{13}{8} - \frac{7}{8} = \boxed{\frac{6}{8}}$$

> I rename $1\frac{5}{8}$ as a fraction greater than 1. I have like units, so I can subtract $\frac{7}{8}$ from $\frac{13}{8}$.

$$\frac{8}{8} - \frac{7}{8} = \frac{1}{8}$$

$$\frac{1}{8} + \frac{5}{8} = \boxed{\frac{6}{8}}$$

> Or, I can subtract $\frac{7}{8}$ from $\frac{8}{8}$, or 1, first and then add the remaining part of the number bond, $\frac{5}{8}$.

EUREKA MATH™   **Lesson 17:**   Use visual models to add and subtract two fractions with the same units, including subtracting from one whole.   23

G4-M5-Lesson 18

Show two ways to solve each problem. Express the answer as a mixed number when possible. Use a number bond when it helps you.

1. $\frac{2}{5} + \frac{3}{5} + \frac{1}{5}$

$$\frac{2}{5} + \frac{3}{5} = \frac{5}{5} = 1$$

$$1 + \frac{1}{5} = 1\frac{1}{5}$$

$$\frac{2}{5} + \frac{3}{5} + \frac{1}{5} = \frac{6}{5} = 1\frac{1}{5}$$

$\frac{5}{5}$ $\frac{1}{5}$

Since the units, or denominators, are the same for each addend, fifths, I can just add the number of units, or numerators.

I can add $\frac{2}{5}$ and $\frac{3}{5}$ to make 1. Then, I can just add $\frac{1}{5}$ more to get $1\frac{1}{5}$.

I can use a number bond to decompose $\frac{6}{5}$ into $\frac{5}{5}$ and $\frac{1}{5}$. Since $\frac{5}{5} = 1$, I can rewrite $\frac{6}{5}$ as $1\frac{1}{5}$.

2. $1 - \frac{3}{12} - \frac{4}{12}$

I add $\frac{3}{12}$ and $\frac{4}{12}$ to get $\frac{7}{12}$. I need to subtract a total of $\frac{7}{12}$ from 1.

$$\frac{3}{12} + \frac{4}{12} = \frac{7}{12}$$

$$\frac{12}{12} - \frac{7}{12} = \frac{5}{12}$$

$$\frac{12}{12} - \frac{3}{12} = \frac{9}{12}$$

$$\frac{9}{12} - \frac{4}{12} = \frac{5}{12}$$

I can rename 1 as $\frac{12}{12}$, and I can subtract $\frac{7}{12}$ from $\frac{12}{12}$.

I rename 1 as $\frac{12}{12}$. Then, I subtract $\frac{3}{12}$, and finally I subtract $\frac{4}{12}$.

EUREKA
MATH™

G4-M5-Lesson 19

Use the RDW process to solve.

1. Noah drank $\frac{8}{10}$ liter of water on Monday and $\frac{6}{10}$ liter on Tuesday. How many liters of water did Noah drink in the 2 days?

w

$\frac{8}{10}$	$\frac{6}{10}$

$\frac{8}{10} + \frac{6}{10} = w$

> I add the parts in my tape diagram to find the total amount of water that Noah drank.

> I draw a tape diagram to model the problem. The parts in my tape diagram represent the water Noah drank on Monday and Tuesday. I use the variable w to represent the liters of water Noah drank on Monday and Tuesday.

$\frac{8}{10} + \frac{6}{10} = \frac{14}{10} = 1\frac{4}{10}$

$\frac{10}{10}$ $\frac{4}{10}$

> Since the addends have like units, I add the numerators to get $\frac{14}{10}$. I use a number bond to decompose $\frac{14}{10}$ into a whole number and a fraction. This helps me rename $\frac{14}{10}$ as a mixed number.

$w = 1\frac{4}{10}$

Noah drank $1\frac{4}{10}$ liters of water.

> I write a statement to answer the question. I also think about the reasonableness of my answer. The water drunk on each day is less than 1 liter, so I would expect to get a total less than 2 liters. My answer of $1\frac{4}{10}$ liters is a reasonable total amount.

2. Muneeb had 2 chapters to read for homework. By 9:00 p.m., he had read $1\frac{2}{7}$ chapters. What fraction of chapters is left for Muneeb to read?

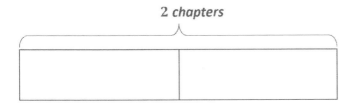

2 chapters

I can draw a tape diagram with 2 equal parts to represent the 2 chapters of the book.

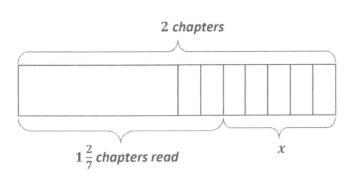

2 chapters

$1\frac{2}{7}$ *chapters read* x

To show $1\frac{2}{7}$ on my tape diagram, I partition one chapter into sevenths. I label the amount that Muneeb has read and the amount that is left, x.

$2 - 1\frac{2}{7} = x$

The unknown in my tape diagram is one of the parts, so I subtract the known part, $1\frac{2}{7}$, from the whole, 2.

$2 - 1\frac{2}{7} = \frac{5}{7}$

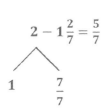

$1 \qquad \frac{7}{7}$

I use a number bond to show how to decompose one of the chapters into sevenths. My tape diagram shows that there is $\frac{5}{7}$ of a chapter left. My equation shows that, too!

$x = \frac{5}{7}$

Muneeb has $\frac{5}{7}$ chapter left to read.

Muneeb started with 2 chapters to read. He read 1 chapter and a little more, so he should have less than 1 chapter left. My answer of $\frac{5}{7}$ chapter is a reasonable amount left because it's less than 1 chapter.

EUREKA MATH

G4-M5-Lesson 20

1. Use a tape diagram to represent each addend. Decompose one of the tape diagrams to make like units. Then, write the complete number sentence.

   $\frac{1}{2} + \frac{3}{8}$

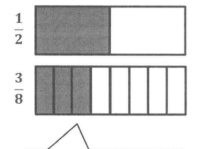

$\frac{1}{2}$

$\frac{3}{8}$

> I draw tape diagrams to model each addend.

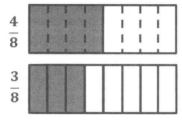

$\frac{4}{8}$

$\frac{3}{8}$

> I make like units by decomposing the halves to make eighths.

$\frac{4}{8} + \frac{3}{8} = \frac{7}{8}$

2. Estimate to determine if the sum is between 0 and 1 or 1 and 2. Draw a number line to model the addition. Then, write a complete number sentence.

   $\frac{7}{10} + \frac{1}{2}$

   > $\frac{7}{10}$ is a little bit more than $\frac{1}{2}$. When I add a fraction that is a little bigger than $\frac{1}{2}$ to $\frac{1}{2}$, I should get a total that is between 1 and 2.

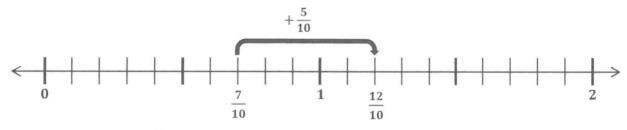

$+\frac{5}{10}$

$0 \qquad \frac{7}{10} \qquad 1 \qquad \frac{12}{10} \qquad 2$

$\frac{7}{10} + \frac{5}{10} = \frac{12}{10}$

> To make like units in order to add, I decompose halves. The number line and the number sentence show the total, $\frac{12}{10}$, which is between 1 and 2.

EUREKA MATH   **Lesson 20:**   Use visual models to add two fractions with related units using the denominators 2, 3, 4, 5, 6, 8, 10, and 12.   27

©2015 Great Minds. eureka-math.org
G4-M1-HWH-1.3.0-07.2015

3. Solve the following addition problem without drawing a model. Show your work.

$$\frac{2}{3} + \frac{1}{9}$$

$$\frac{2}{3} = \frac{2 \times 3}{3 \times 3} = \frac{6}{9}$$

> I can decompose thirds to make ninths by multiplying the numerator and denominator of $\frac{2}{3}$ by 3.

$$\frac{6}{9} + \frac{1}{9} = \frac{7}{9}$$

> Now, I have like units, ninths, and I can add.

EUREKA
MATH

G4-M5-Lesson 21

1. Use a tape diagram to represent each addend. Decompose one of the tape diagrams to make like units. Then, write the complete number sentence. Use a number bond to write the sum as a mixed number.

$\dfrac{5}{6} + \dfrac{2}{3}$

$\dfrac{5}{6}$

$\dfrac{2}{3}$ $\dfrac{4}{6}$

> I add now that I have like units.

$\dfrac{5}{6} + \dfrac{4}{6} = \dfrac{9}{6} = 1\dfrac{3}{6}$

$\dfrac{6}{6}$ $\dfrac{3}{6}$

> I can make like units by decomposing the thirds as sixths. I decompose the thirds because they are the larger unit (thirds > sixths).

2. Draw a number line to model the addition. Then, write a complete number sentence. Use a number bond to write the sum as a mixed number.

$\dfrac{1}{2} + \dfrac{7}{8}$

$\dfrac{1}{2} = \dfrac{1 \times 4}{2 \times 4} = \dfrac{4}{8}$

> I rename halves as eighths to make like units to add.

$\dfrac{4}{8} + \dfrac{7}{8} = \dfrac{11}{8} = 1\dfrac{3}{8}$

$\dfrac{8}{8}$ $\dfrac{3}{8}$

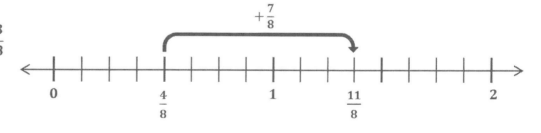

$+\dfrac{7}{8}$

0            $\dfrac{4}{8}$ 1 $\dfrac{11}{8}$ 2

3. Solve. Write the sum as a mixed number. Draw a model if needed.

$\dfrac{5}{6} + \dfrac{2}{3}$

$\dfrac{5}{6} + \dfrac{2}{3} = \dfrac{5}{6} + \dfrac{4}{6} = \dfrac{9}{6} = 1\dfrac{3}{6}$

$\dfrac{6}{6}$ $\dfrac{3}{6}$

> I double the units (denominator) to make sixths, which means I also need to double the number of units (numerator). $\dfrac{2}{3}$ is equal to $\dfrac{4}{6}$.

G4-M5-Lesson 22

1. Draw a tape diagram to match the number sentence. Then, complete the number sentence.

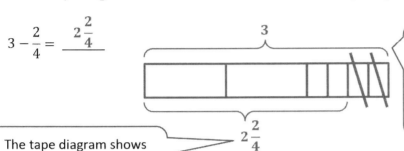

$$3 - \frac{2}{4} = \underline{2\frac{2}{4}}$$

I draw a tape diagram with 3 equal units, with 1 unit decomposed into fourths. To show the subtraction, I cross off $\frac{2}{4}$.

$2\frac{2}{4}$

The tape diagram shows the difference is $2\frac{2}{4}$.

2. Use $\frac{5}{6}$, 3, and $2\frac{1}{6}$ to write two subtraction and two addition number sentences.

$$\frac{5}{6} + 2\frac{1}{6} = 3$$

$$2\frac{1}{6} + \frac{5}{6} = 3$$

$$3 - \frac{5}{6} = 2\frac{1}{6}$$

$$3 - 2\frac{1}{6} = \frac{5}{6}$$

I can also represent the relationship between these 3 numbers with a number bond.

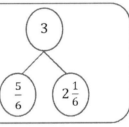

3. Solve using a number bond. Draw a number line to represent the number sentence.

$$4 - \frac{2}{3} = \underline{3\frac{1}{3}}$$

$$4 - \frac{2}{3} = 3\frac{1}{3}$$

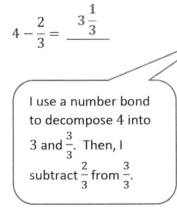

I use a number bond to decompose 4 into 3 and $\frac{3}{3}$. Then, I subtract $\frac{2}{3}$ from $\frac{3}{3}$.

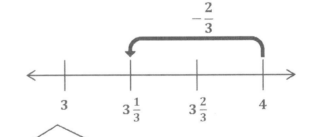

I draw a number line with the endpoints 3 and 4 because I am starting at 4 and subtracting a number less than 1.

     Lesson 22:   Add a fraction less than 1 to, or subtract a fraction less than 1 from, a whole number using decomposition and visual models.

EUREKA MATH™

4. Complete the subtraction sentence using a number bond.

$6 - \dfrac{6}{8} =$ _____ $5\dfrac{2}{8}$

Number bond: 6 branches to 5 and $\dfrac{8}{8}$

$\dfrac{8}{8} - \dfrac{6}{8} = \dfrac{2}{8}$

$5 + \dfrac{2}{8} = 5\dfrac{2}{8}$

I subtract $\dfrac{6}{8}$ from $\dfrac{8}{8}$ to get $\dfrac{2}{8}$. I add $\dfrac{2}{8}$ back to 5.

EUREKA MATH   **Lesson 22:**   Add a fraction less than 1 to, or subtract a fraction less than 1 from, a whole number using decomposition and visual models.   31

©2015 Great Minds. eureka-math.org
G4-M1-HWH-1.3.0-07.2015

G4-M5-Lesson 23

1. Count by 1 fifths. Start at 0 fifths. End at 10 fifths. Circle any fractions that are equivalent to a whole number. Record the whole number below the fraction.

$$\left(\frac{0}{5}\right), \frac{1}{5}, \frac{2}{5}, \frac{3}{5}, \frac{4}{5}, \left(\frac{5}{5}\right), \frac{6}{5}, \frac{7}{5}, \frac{8}{5}, \frac{9}{5}, \left(\frac{10}{5}\right)$$

0   1   2

> I know that 5 fifths equals 1, so 10 fifths equals 2.

2. Use parentheses to show how to make ones in the following number sentence.

$$\left(\frac{1}{4} + \frac{1}{4} + \frac{1}{4} + \frac{1}{4}\right) + \left(\frac{1}{4} + \frac{1}{4} + \frac{1}{4} + \frac{1}{4}\right) = 2$$

> I draw parentheses around groups of 4 fourths because the denominator (fourths) tells me how many unit fractions composed make 1.

3. Multiply. Draw a number line to support your answer.

$$4 \times \frac{1}{2}$$

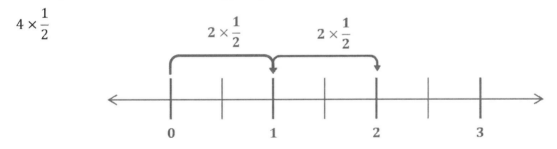

$2 \times \frac{1}{2}$ $2 \times \frac{1}{2}$

0   1   2   3

$$4 \times \frac{1}{2} = 2 \times \frac{2}{2} = 2$$

> I see on my number line that 4 copies of $\frac{1}{2}$ is the same as 2 copies of $\frac{2}{2}$. Since $\frac{2}{2}$ is the same as 1, I think of 2 copies of $\frac{2}{2}$ as the multiplication sentence, $2 \times 1 = 2$. So, $4 \times \frac{1}{2} = 2$.

Lesson 23:   Add and multiply unit fractions to build fractions greater than 1
                                using visual models.

EUREKA
MATH

4. Multiply. Write the product as a mixed number. Draw a number line to support your answer.

$11 \times \dfrac{1}{4}$

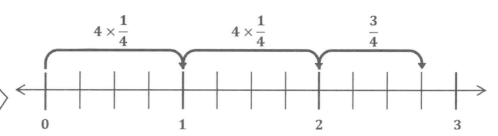

$4 \times \dfrac{1}{4}$ $4 \times \dfrac{1}{4}$ $\dfrac{3}{4}$

> I draw a number line and partition each whole into fourths since the fractional unit that I'm multiplying by is fourths.

$$11 \times \frac{1}{4} = \left(2 \times \frac{4}{4}\right) + \frac{3}{4} = 2 + \frac{3}{4} = 2\frac{3}{4}$$

> I can see on my number line that 11 copies of $\dfrac{1}{4}$ equals 2 copies of $\dfrac{4}{4}$ plus $\dfrac{3}{4}$.

EUREKA MATH   **Lesson 23:**   Add and multiply unit fractions to build fractions greater than 1 using visual models.   33

©2015 Great Minds. eureka-math.org
G4-M1-HWH-1.3.0-07.2015

G4-M5-Lesson 24

1. Rename $\frac{10}{3}$ as a mixed number by decomposing it into two parts. Model the decomposition with a number line and a number bond.

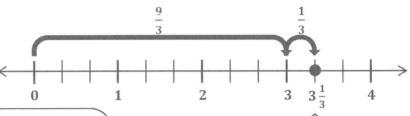

$$\frac{10}{3} = \frac{9}{3} + \frac{1}{3} = 3 + \frac{1}{3} = 3\frac{1}{3}$$

$\frac{9}{3}$ $\frac{1}{3}$

> I choose the 2 parts $\frac{9}{3}$ and $\frac{1}{3}$ for the number bond because $\frac{9}{3}$ is 3 groups of $\frac{3}{3}$, or 3. Then, I add the other part of my number bond, $\frac{1}{3}$, to get the mixed number $3\frac{1}{3}$.

> The number line shows that decomposing $\frac{10}{3}$ as $\frac{9}{3}$ and $\frac{1}{3}$ is the same as $3\frac{1}{3}$.

2. Rename $\frac{8}{3}$ as a mixed number using multiplication. Draw a number line to support your answer.

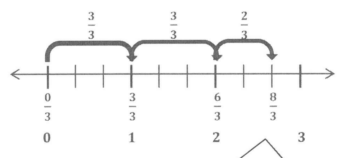

$$\frac{8}{3} = \frac{3 \times 2}{3} + \frac{2}{3} = 2 + \frac{2}{3} = 2\frac{2}{3}$$

> I use multiplication to show that $\frac{6}{3}$ is 2 copies of $\frac{3}{3}$, which is the same as 2.

> The number line supports $\frac{8}{3}$ renamed as $2\frac{2}{3}$. They are equal.

3. Convert $\frac{22}{7}$ to a mixed number.

$$\frac{22}{7} = \left(3 \times \frac{7}{7}\right) + \frac{1}{7} = 3 + \frac{1}{7} = 3\frac{1}{7}$$

> I can make 3 groups of $\frac{7}{7}$, which equals $\frac{21}{7}$.
> I can add 1 more seventh to equal $\frac{22}{7}$.

Lesson 24:   Decompose and compose fractions greater than 1 to express them in various forms.

G4-M5-Lesson 25

1. Convert the mixed number $2\frac{2}{4}$ to a fraction greater than 1. Draw a number line to model your work.

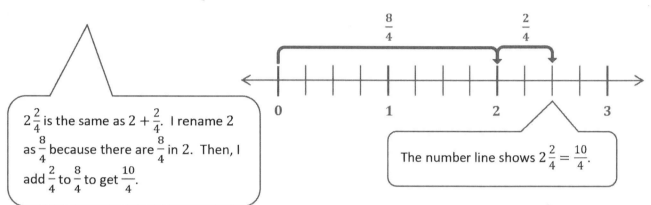

$2\frac{2}{4}$ is the same as $2 + \frac{2}{4}$. I rename 2 as $\frac{8}{4}$ because there are $\frac{8}{4}$ in 2. Then, I add $\frac{2}{4}$ to $\frac{8}{4}$ to get $\frac{10}{4}$.

The number line shows $2\frac{2}{4} = \frac{10}{4}$.

2. Use multiplication to convert the mixed number $5\frac{1}{4}$ to a fraction greater than 1.

$$5\frac{1}{4} = 5 + \frac{1}{4} = \left(5 \times \frac{4}{4}\right) + \frac{1}{4} = \frac{20}{4} + \frac{1}{4} = \frac{21}{4}$$

I rewrite 5 as the multiplication expression, $5 \times \frac{4}{4}$. Then, I can multiply $5 \times \frac{4}{4}$ to get $\frac{20}{4}$. So, there are $\frac{20}{4}$ in 5. Then, I add the $\frac{1}{4}$ from the $5\frac{1}{4}$ to get $\frac{21}{4}$.

3. Convert the mixed number $6\frac{1}{3}$ to a fraction greater than 1.

$$6\frac{1}{3} = \frac{18}{3} + \frac{1}{3} = \frac{19}{3}$$

I use mental math. There are 6 ones and 1 third in the number $6\frac{1}{3}$. I know that there are 18 thirds in 6 ones. 18 thirds plus 1 more third is 19 thirds.

EUREKA MATH™

Lesson 25: Decompose and compose fractions greater than 1 to express them in various forms.

35

©2015 Great Minds. eureka-math.org
G4-M1-HWH-1.3.0-07.2015

G4-M5-Lesson 26

1.

a. Plot the following points on the number line without measuring.

  i. $6\frac{7}{8}$ ii. $\frac{36}{5} = 7\frac{1}{5}$ iii. $\frac{19}{3} = 6\frac{1}{3}$

> To plot the numbers on the number line, I rewrite $\frac{36}{5}$ and $\frac{19}{3}$ as mixed numbers.

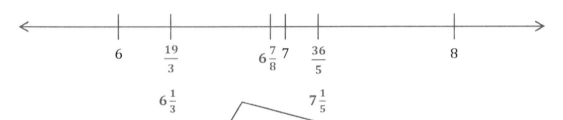

  6 $\frac{19}{3}$ $6\frac{7}{8}$ 7 $\frac{36}{5}$ 8

        $6\frac{1}{3}$ $7\frac{1}{5}$

> I estimate to plot each number on the number line. I know that $6\frac{7}{8}$ is $\frac{1}{8}$ less than 7. I use this strategy to plot $6\frac{1}{3}$ and $7\frac{1}{5}$.

b. Use the number line in Part 1(a) to compare the numbers by writing >, <, or =.

  i. $\frac{19}{3}$ ___<___ $6\frac{7}{8}$ ii. $\frac{36}{5}$ ___>___ $\frac{19}{3}$

> I remember from Lessons 12 and 13 how I used the benchmarks of 0, $\frac{1}{2}$, and 1 to compare. $\frac{19}{3}$ is less than $6\frac{1}{2}$, and $6\frac{7}{8}$ is greater than $6\frac{1}{2}$. $\frac{36}{5}$ is greater than 7 and $\frac{19}{3}$ is less than 7.

Lesson 26:   Compare fractions greater than 1 by reasoning using benchmark
                    fractions.

EUREKA
MATH

2. Compare the fractions given below by writing $>$, $<$, or $=$. Give a brief explanation for each answer, referring to benchmark fractions.

a. $4\frac{4}{8}$ ____$>$____ $4\frac{2}{5}$

   $4\frac{4}{8}$ is the same as $4\frac{1}{2}$. $4\frac{2}{5}$ is less than $4\frac{1}{2}$, so $4\frac{4}{8}$ is greater than $4\frac{2}{5}$.

b. $\frac{43}{9}$ ____$<$____ $\frac{35}{7}$

   $\frac{35}{7}$ is the same as 5. $\frac{43}{9}$ needs 2 more ninths to equal 5. That means that $\frac{35}{7}$ is greater than $\frac{43}{9}$.

G4-M5-Lesson 27

1. Draw a tape diagram to model the comparison. Use >, <, or = to compare.

$5\dfrac{7}{8}$ ___>___ $\dfrac{23}{4}$

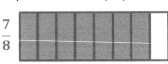

$\dfrac{7}{8}$

$\dfrac{23}{4} = 5\dfrac{3}{4}$

$\dfrac{3}{4} = \dfrac{6}{8}$

$\dfrac{20}{4}$ $\dfrac{3}{4}$

I can rename $\dfrac{23}{4}$ as a mixed number, $5\dfrac{3}{4}$.

Since both numbers have 5 ones, I draw tape diagrams to represent the fractional parts of each number. I decompose fourths to eighths. My tape diagrams show that $\dfrac{3}{4} = \dfrac{6}{8}$ and $\dfrac{7}{8} > \dfrac{6}{8}$.

2. Use an area model to make like units. Then, use >, <, or = to compare.

$4\dfrac{2}{3}$ ___>___ $\dfrac{23}{5}$

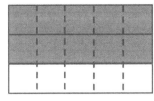

$\dfrac{23}{5} = 4\dfrac{3}{5}$

$\dfrac{2}{3} = \dfrac{10}{15}$

$\dfrac{20}{5}$ $\dfrac{3}{5}$

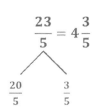

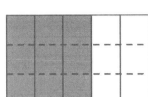

$\dfrac{3}{5} = \dfrac{9}{15}$

I draw area models to represent the fractional parts of each number. I make like units by drawing fifths vertically on the thirds and thirds horizontally on the fifths.

Lesson 27:   Compare fractions greater than 1 by creating common numerators
                    or denominators.

EUREKA MATH™

3. Compare each pair of fractions using >, <, or = using any strategy.

a. $\dfrac{14}{6}$ _____ > _____ $\dfrac{14}{9}$

Both fractions have the same numerator. Since sixths are bigger than ninths, $\dfrac{14}{6} > \dfrac{14}{9}$.

b. $\dfrac{19}{4}$ _____ < _____ $\dfrac{25}{5}$

$\dfrac{25}{5} = 5$, and $\dfrac{19}{4} < 5$ because is takes 20 fourths to equal 5.

c. $6\dfrac{2}{6}$ _____ > _____ $6\dfrac{4}{9}$

$$\dfrac{2 \times 3}{6 \times 3} = \dfrac{6}{18}$$

$$\dfrac{4 \times 2}{9 \times 2} = \dfrac{8}{18}$$

$$\dfrac{6}{18} < \dfrac{8}{18}$$

I make like units, eighteenths, and compare.

G4-M5-Lesson 28

1. A group of students recorded the amount of time they spent doing homework in a week. The times are shown in the table. Make a line plot to display the data.

Student	Time Spent Doing Homework (in hours)	
Rebecca	$6\frac{1}{4}$	✓
Noah	6	✓
Wilson	$5\frac{3}{4}$	✓
Jenna	$6\frac{1}{4}$	✓
Sam	$6\frac{1}{2}$	✓
Angie	6	✓
Matthew	$6\frac{1}{4}$	✓
Jessica	$6\frac{3}{4}$	✓

> I can make a line plot with an interval of fourths because that's the smallest unit in the table. My endpoints are $5\frac{3}{4}$ and $6\frac{3}{4}$ because those are the shortest and longest times spent doing homework. I can draw an X above the correct time on the number line to represent the time each student spent doing homework.

Time Spent Doing Homework in One Week

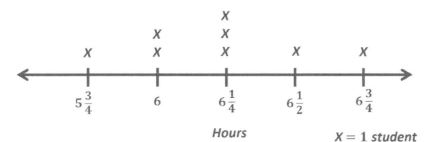

Hours

X = 1 student

2. Solve each problem.

   a. Who spent 1 hour longer doing homework than Wilson?

   $$5\frac{3}{4} + 1 = 6\frac{3}{4}$$

   > I can add 1 hour to Wilson's time and look at the table to find the answer.

   Jessica spent 1 hour longer doing homework than Wilson.

   b. How many quarter hours did Jenna spend doing homework?

   $$6\frac{1}{4} = \frac{24}{4} + \frac{1}{4} = \frac{25}{4}$$

   Jenna spent 25 quarter hours doing her homework.

Lesson 28: Solve word problems with line plots.

EUREKA MATH

c.   What is the difference, in hours, between the most frequent amount of time spent doing homework and the second most frequent amount of time spent doing homework?

$$6\frac{1}{4} - 6 = \frac{1}{4}$$

The difference is 1 fourth hour.

> The X's on the line plot help me see the most frequent time, $6\frac{1}{4}$ hours, and the second most frequent time, 6 hours.

d.   Compare the times of Matthew and Sam using >, <, or =.

$$6\frac{1}{4} < 6\frac{1}{2}$$

Matthew spent less time doing his homework than Sam.

e.   How many students spent less than $6\frac{1}{2}$ hours doing their homework?

Six students spent less than $6\frac{1}{2}$ hours doing their homework.

> I can count the X's on the line plot for $5\frac{3}{4}$ hours, 6 hours, and $6\frac{1}{4}$ hours.

f.   How many students recorded the amount of time they spent doing their homework?

Eight students recorded the amount of time they spent doing their homework.

> I can count the X's on the line plot, or I can count the students in the table.

g.   Scott spent $\frac{30}{4}$ hours in one week doing his homework. Use >, <, or = to compare Scott's time to the time of the student who spent the most hours doing homework. Who spent more time doing homework?

$$\frac{30}{4} = \frac{28}{4} + \frac{2}{4} = 7 + \frac{2}{4} = 7\frac{2}{4}$$

$$7\frac{2}{4} > 6\frac{3}{4}$$

> I can rename Scott's time as a mixed number, and then I can compare (or I can rename Jessica's time as a fraction greater than 1). There are 7 ones in Scott's time and only 6 ones in Jessica's time.

Scott spent more time than Jessica doing homework.

G4-M5-Lesson 29

1. Estimate each sum or difference to the nearest half or whole number by rounding. Explain your estimate using words or a number line.

    a. $4\frac{1}{9} + 2\frac{4}{5} \approx$ ___7___

    $4\frac{1}{9}$ *is close to* 4, *and* $2\frac{4}{5}$ *is close to* 3. $4 + 3 = 7$

    > $4\frac{1}{9}$ is 1 ninth more than 4. $2\frac{4}{5}$ is 1 fifth less than 3.

    b. $7\frac{5}{6} - 2\frac{1}{4} \approx$ ___6___

    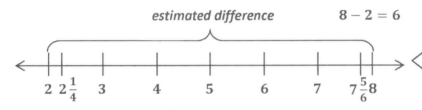

    estimated difference $8 - 2 = 6$

    > I draw a number line and plot the mixed numbers. It's easy to see on my number line that $7\frac{5}{6}$ is close to 8 and $2\frac{1}{4}$ is close to 2.

    > My number line makes it easy to see that the estimated difference is larger than the actual difference because I rounded one number up and the other number down.

    c. $5\frac{4}{10} + 3\frac{1}{8} \approx$ ___$8\frac{1}{2}$___

    $5\frac{4}{10}$ *is close to* $5\frac{1}{2}$, *and* $3\frac{1}{8}$ *is close to* 3. $5\frac{1}{2} + 3 = 8\frac{1}{2}$

    d. $\frac{15}{7} + \frac{20}{3} \approx$ ___9___ $\frac{15}{7} = 2\frac{1}{7}$ $\frac{20}{3} = 6\frac{2}{3}$

    $2 + 7 = 9$ $2\frac{1}{7} \approx 2$ $6\frac{2}{3} \approx 7$

    I renamed each fraction greater than 1 as a mixed number. Then, I rounded to the nearest whole number and added the rounded numbers.

EUREKA MATH

2. Ben's estimate for $8\frac{6}{10} - 3\frac{1}{4}$ was 6. Michelle's estimate was $5\frac{1}{2}$. Whose estimate do you think is closer to the actual difference? Explain.

I think Michelle's estimate is closer to the actual difference. Ben rounded both numbers to the nearest whole number and then subtracted: $9 - 3 = 6$. Michelle rounded $8\frac{6}{10}$ to the nearest half, $8\frac{1}{2}$, and she rounded $3\frac{1}{4}$ to the nearest whole number. Then, she subtracted: $8\frac{1}{2} - 3 = 5\frac{1}{2}$. Since $8\frac{6}{10}$ is closer to $8\frac{1}{2}$ than 9, rounding it to the nearest half will give a closer estimate than rounding both numbers to the nearest whole number.

I can also draw number lines to show the actual difference, Ben's estimated difference, and Michelle's estimated difference. Because Ben rounded the total up and the part down, his estimated difference will be greater than the actual difference.

3. Use benchmark numbers or mental math to estimate the sum.

$14\frac{3}{8} + 7\frac{7}{12} \approx 22$

$14\frac{1}{2} + 7\frac{1}{2} = 21 + 1 = 22$

$\frac{3}{8}$ is 1 eighth less than $\frac{1}{2}$, and $\frac{7}{12}$ is 1 twelfth greater than $\frac{1}{2}$. I add the ones, and then I add the halves to get 22.

G4-M5-Lesson 30

1. Solve.

$6\frac{2}{5} + \frac{3}{5} = 6\frac{5}{5} = 7$

> I add using unit form. 6 ones 2 fifths + 3 fifths = 6 ones 5 fifths.
> I know that $\frac{5}{5} = 1$, so $6 + 1 = 7$.

2. Complete the number sentence.

$18 = 17\frac{3}{10} + \frac{7}{10}$

> I know that $17 + 1 = 18$, so I need to find a fraction that equals 1 when added to $\frac{3}{10}$. $3 + 7 = 10$, so the fraction that completes the number sentence is 7 tenths.

3. Use a number bond and the arrow way to show how to make one. Solve.

$3\frac{5}{8} + \frac{6}{8}$

> I decompose $\frac{6}{8}$ into $\frac{3}{8}$ and $\frac{3}{8}$ because I know $3\frac{5}{8}$ needs $\frac{3}{8}$ to make the next whole number, 4.

$3\frac{5}{8} \xrightarrow{+\frac{3}{8}} 4 \xrightarrow{+\frac{3}{8}} 4\frac{3}{8}$

> The arrow way reminds me of making ten or making change from a dollar.

4. Solve.

$\frac{7}{8} + 4\frac{6}{8}$

$\frac{7}{8} + 4\frac{6}{8} = 4\frac{13}{8} = 5\frac{5}{8}$

> I can add using any method that makes sense to me, like adding in unit form, using the arrow method, or adding to make the next 1, as shown below.
>
> $\frac{7}{8} + 4\frac{6}{8} = \frac{5}{8} + 5 = 5\frac{5}{8}$
>

Lesson 30:   Add a mixed number and a fraction.

EUREKA MATH

©2015 Great Minds. eureka-math.org
G4-M1-HWH-1.3.0-07.2015

G4-M5-Lesson 31

1. Solve.

$$3\frac{1}{5} + 2\frac{4}{5}$$

I can add like units. 3 ones 1 fifth + 2 ones 4 fifths = 5 ones 5 fifths.

$$3\frac{1}{5} + 2\frac{4}{5} = 5 + \frac{5}{5} = 5 + 1 = 6$$

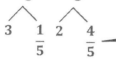

3   $\frac{1}{5}$ 2 $\frac{4}{5}$

I can use number bonds to decompose the numbers into ones and fifths.

2. Solve. Use a number line to show your work.

$$1\frac{2}{3} + 3\frac{2}{3}$$

$$1\frac{2}{3} + 3\frac{2}{3} = 4 + \frac{4}{3} = 5\frac{1}{3}$$

$\frac{3}{3}$ $\frac{1}{3}$

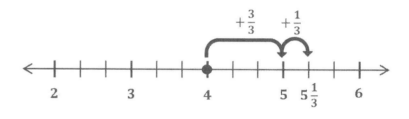

I add the ones and thirds. I decompose $\frac{4}{3}$ into 1 and $\frac{1}{3}$. $4 + 1 + \frac{1}{3} = 5\frac{1}{3}$

3. Solve. Use the arrow way to show how to make one.

$$4\frac{7}{12} + 3\frac{9}{12}$$

$$4\frac{7}{12} + 3\frac{9}{12} = 7\frac{7}{12} + \frac{9}{12} = 8\frac{4}{12}$$

$\frac{5}{12}$ $\frac{4}{12}$

$$7\frac{7}{12} \xrightarrow{+\frac{5}{12}} 8 \xrightarrow{+\frac{4}{12}} 8\frac{4}{12}$$

I use the arrow way to add $\frac{5}{12}$ and $7\frac{7}{12}$ to make the next whole number. Then, I add the other part of the number bond to get $8\frac{4}{12}$.

G4-M5-Lesson 32

1. Subtract. Model with a number line or the arrow way.

$$4\frac{3}{5} - \frac{2}{5} = 4\frac{1}{5}$$

> I can subtract 2 fifths $\frac{1}{5}$ at a time or all at once.

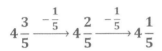

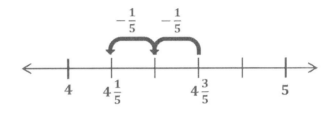

2. Use decomposition to subtract the fractions. Model with a number line or the arrow way.

$$6\frac{2}{6} - \frac{5}{6}$$

> I decompose $\frac{5}{6}$ into $\frac{2}{6}$ and $\frac{3}{6}$ so that I can subtract $\frac{2}{6}$ from $6\frac{2}{6}$ to get to a whole number.

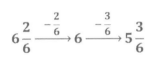

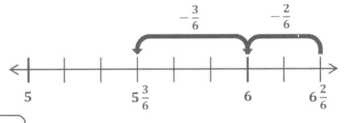

> I subtract the other part of the number bond, $\frac{3}{6}$.

3. Decompose the total to subtract the fraction.

$$8\frac{2}{12} - \frac{9}{12}$$

> There aren't enough twelfths to subtract 9 twelfths, so I decompose the total to subtract $\frac{9}{12}$ from 1.

$$8\frac{2}{12} - \frac{9}{12} = 7\frac{2}{12} + \frac{3}{12} = 7\frac{5}{12}$$

> Once $\frac{9}{12}$ is subtracted, the remaining numbers are added together.

EUREKA MATH

G4-M5-Lesson 33

1. Write a related addition sentence. Subtract by counting on. Use a number line or the arrow way to help.

$$6\frac{1}{4} - 2\frac{3}{4} = 3\frac{2}{4}$$

> I add the numbers on top of the arrows to find the unknown addend.
>
> $$\frac{1}{4} + 3 + \frac{1}{4} = 3\frac{2}{4}$$

$$2\frac{3}{4} + 3\frac{2}{4} = 6\frac{1}{4}$$

$$2\frac{3}{4} \xrightarrow{+\frac{1}{4}} 3 \xrightarrow{+3} 6 \xrightarrow{+\frac{1}{4}} 6\frac{1}{4}$$

> I add 3 to get to 6.

> I use the arrow way to count up to solve for the unknown in my addition sentence. I add $\frac{1}{4}$ to get to the next one, 3.

> My final number needs to be $6\frac{1}{4}$, so I need to add 1 more fourth.

2. Subtract by decomposing the fractional part of the number you are subtracting. Use a number line or the arrow way to help you.

$$4\frac{1}{3} - 1\frac{2}{3} = 3\frac{1}{3} - \frac{2}{3} = 2\frac{2}{3}$$

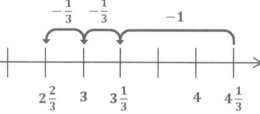

> I subtract 1 from $4\frac{1}{3}$.

> $3\frac{1}{3} - \frac{1}{3} = 3$ and $3 - \frac{1}{3} = 2\frac{2}{3}$.

3. Subtract by decomposing to take one out.

$7\frac{2}{10} - 5\frac{9}{10}$

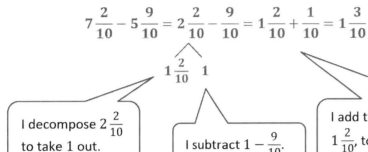

$$7\frac{2}{10} - 5\frac{9}{10} = 2\frac{2}{10} - \frac{9}{10} = 1\frac{2}{10} + \frac{1}{10} = 1\frac{3}{10}$$

I decompose $2\frac{2}{10}$ to take 1 out.

I subtract $1 - \frac{9}{10}$.

I add the other part of the number bond, $1\frac{2}{10}$, to the difference of $1 - \frac{9}{10}$.

EUREKA MATH™

G4-M5-Lesson 34

1. Subtract.

$$8\frac{2}{7} - \frac{6}{7} = 7\frac{9}{7} - \frac{6}{7} = 7\frac{3}{7}$$

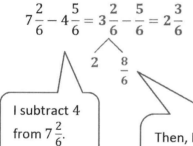

7    $\frac{9}{7}$

Now I have 9 sevenths, which is enough sevenths to subtract 6 sevenths.

It's just like renaming 1 ten for 10 ones when subtracting whole numbers, except I rename 1 one for 7 sevenths.

2. Subtract the ones first.

$$7\frac{2}{6} - 4\frac{5}{6} = 3\frac{2}{6} - \frac{5}{6} = 2\frac{3}{6}$$

2    $\frac{8}{6}$

I subtract 4 from $7\frac{2}{6}$.

Then, I decompose $3\frac{2}{6}$ to rename enough sixths to subtract 5 sixths.

$$7\frac{2}{6} \xrightarrow{-4} 3\frac{2}{6} \xrightarrow{-\frac{5}{6}} 2\frac{3}{6}$$

I can show the same work with the arrow way.

©2015 Great Minds. eureka-math.org
G4-M1-HWH-1.3.0-07.2015

G4-M5-Lesson 35

1. Draw and label a tape diagram to show the following is true:

   10 fourths = 5 × (2 fourths) = (5 × 2) fourths

   > I can move the parentheses in the equation, associating the factors, 5 and 2. When I do so, fourths becomes the unit.

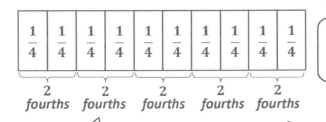

   > I can do this with any unit:
   > 10 bananas = 5 × (2 bananas) = (5 × 2) bananas.

   > Using brackets to group every 2 units of $\frac{1}{4}$, I model 5 copies of 2 fourths.

   > The product of 5 and 2 is 10. My model shows that (5 × 2) fourths is the same as 5 × (2 fourths), or 10 fourths.

2. Write the equation in unit form to solve.

   $$8 \times \frac{2}{3} = \frac{16}{3}$$

   $8 \times 2 \ thirds = 16 \ thirds$

   > Unit form simplifies my multiplication. Instead of puzzling over how to multiply a fraction by a whole number, I unveil an easy fact I can solve fast! I know 8 × 2 is 16, so 8 × 2 thirds is 16 thirds.

3. Solve.

   $$6 \times \frac{3}{4}$$

   > The unit is fourths! I think in unit form, 6 × 3 fourths is 18 fourths.

   $$6 \times \frac{3}{4} = \frac{6 \times 3}{4} = \frac{18}{4}$$

Lesson 35:   Represent the multiplication of *n* times *a/b* as (*n* × *a*)/*b* using the associative property and visual models.

EUREKA MATH™

4. Ms. Swanson bought some apple juice. Each member of her family drank $\frac{3}{5}$ cup for breakfast. Including Ms. Swanson, there are four people in her family. How many cups of apple juice did they drink?

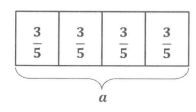

$$a = 4 \times \frac{3}{5}$$

$$= \frac{4 \times 3}{5}$$

$$= \frac{12}{5}$$

$$a = 2\frac{2}{5}$$

Ms. Swanson and her family drank $2\frac{2}{5}$ cups of apple juice.

EUREKA MATH

Lesson 35: Represent the multiplication of *n* times *a/b* as (*n* × *a*)/*b* using the associative property and visual models.

51

©2015 Great Minds. eureka-math.org
G4-M1-HWH-1.3.0-07.2015

G4-M5-Lesson 36

1. Draw a tape diagram to represent $\frac{3}{8} + \frac{3}{8} + \frac{3}{8} + \frac{3}{8}$.

$\frac{3}{8}$	$\frac{3}{8}$	$\frac{3}{8}$	$\frac{3}{8}$

I model 4 copies of $\frac{3}{8}$.

Write a multiplication expression equal to $\frac{3}{8} + \frac{3}{8} + \frac{3}{8} + \frac{3}{8}$.

$$4 \times \frac{3}{8} = \frac{12}{8} = 1\frac{4}{8} = 1\frac{1}{2}$$

Multiplication is more efficient than addition. I can solve easily by thinking in unit form: 4×3 eighths is 12 eighths.

2. Solve using any method. Express your answers as whole or mixed numbers.

a. $4 \times \frac{5}{8}$

$\frac{5}{8}$	$\frac{5}{8}$	$\frac{5}{8}$	$\frac{5}{8}$

$$4 \times \frac{5}{8} = \frac{4 \times 5}{8} = \frac{20}{8} = 2\frac{4}{8} = 2\frac{1}{2}$$

b. $32 \times \frac{2}{5}$

$$32 \times \frac{2}{5} = 32 \times 2 \text{ fifths} = 64 \text{ fifths} = \frac{64}{5} = 12\frac{4}{5}$$

To solve, I think to myself, 5 times what number is close to or equal to 64? Or, I can divide 64 by 5.

3. A bricklayer places 13 bricks end to end along the entire outside length of a shed's wall. Each brick is $\frac{2}{3}$ foot long. How long is that wall of the shed?

$\frac{2}{3}$	$\frac{2}{3}$	$\frac{2}{3}$	$\frac{2}{3}$	$\frac{2}{3}$	$\frac{2}{3}$	$\frac{2}{3}$	$\frac{2}{3}$	$\frac{2}{3}$	$\frac{2}{3}$	$\frac{2}{3}$	$\frac{2}{3}$	$\frac{2}{3}$

s

$$13 \times \frac{2}{3} = \frac{13 \times 2}{3} = \frac{26}{3} = 8\frac{2}{3}$$

The wall of the shed is $8\frac{2}{3}$ feet long.

It would take too long to write an addition sentence to solve! Multiplication is quick and easy!

Lesson 36:   Represent the multiplication of n times a/b as $(n \times a)/b$ using the associative property and visual models.

EUREKA MATH™

©2015 Great Minds. eureka-math.org
G4-M1-HWH-1.3.0-07.2015

G4-M5-Lesson 37

1. Draw tape diagrams to show two ways to represent 3 units of $5\frac{1}{12}$.

$5\frac{1}{12}$	$5\frac{1}{12}$	$5\frac{1}{12}$

5	5	5	$\frac{1}{12}$ $\frac{1}{12}$ $\frac{1}{12}$

> I rearrange the model for 3 copies of $5\frac{1}{12}$ by decomposing $5\frac{1}{12}$ into two parts: 5 and $\frac{1}{12}$. I show 3 groups of 5 and 3 groups of $\frac{1}{12}$.

Write a multiplication expression to match each tape diagram.

$$3 \times 5\frac{1}{12}$$

$$(3 \times 5) + \left(3 \times \frac{1}{12}\right)$$

> $5\frac{1}{12}$ is composed of two units: ones and twelfths. I use the distributive property to multiply the value of each unit by 3. $3 \times 5\frac{1}{12}$ is equal to 3 fives and 3 twelfths.

2. Solve using the distributive property.

a. $2 \times 3\frac{5}{6} = 2 \times \left(3 + \frac{5}{6}\right)$

$$= (2 \times 3) + \left(2 \times \frac{5}{6}\right)$$
$$= 6 + \frac{10}{6}$$
$$= 6 + 1\frac{4}{6}$$
$$= 7\frac{4}{6}$$

> I omit writing this step for Part (b) because I can see it's 4 copies of 2 and 4 copies of $\frac{3}{4}$, or $8 + \frac{12}{4}$.

b. $4 \times 2\frac{3}{4} = 4 \times \left(2 + \frac{3}{4}\right)$

$$= 8 + \frac{12}{4}$$
$$= 8 + 3$$
$$= 11$$

3. Sara's street is $1\frac{3}{5}$ miles long. She ran the length of the street 3 times. How far did she run?

| $1\frac{3}{5}$ | $1\frac{3}{5}$ | $1\frac{3}{5}$ |

$\underbrace{}_{s}$

$s = 3 \times 1\frac{3}{5}$

> I use the distributive property to multiply the ones by 3 and the fractional part by 3.

$= (3 \times 1) + \left(3 \times \frac{3}{5}\right)$

$= 3 + \frac{9}{5}$

$= 3 + 1\frac{4}{5}$

$s = 4\frac{4}{5}$

Sara ran $4\frac{4}{5}$ miles.

Lesson 37:   Find the product of a whole number and a mixed number using the
                           distributive property.

©2015 Great Minds. eureka-math.org
G4-M1-HWH-1.3.0-07.2015

G4-M5-Lesson 38

1. Fill in the unknown factors.

    a. $7 \times 3\frac{4}{5} = (\underline{\ 7\ } \times 3) + (\underline{\ 7\ } \times \frac{4}{5})$

    b. $6 \times 4\frac{3}{8} = (6 \times \underline{\ 4\ }) + (6 \times \underline{\ \frac{3}{8}\ })$

    > The mixed number is distributed as the whole and the fraction. Both of the distributed numbers have to be multiplied by 7, so 7 is the missing factor.

2. Multiply. Use the distributive property.

    $5 \times 7\frac{3}{5}$

7	$\frac{3}{5}$	7	$\frac{3}{5}$	7	$\frac{3}{5}$	7	$\frac{3}{5}$	7	$\frac{3}{5}$

    $$5 \times 7\frac{3}{5} = 35 + \frac{15}{5}$$
    $$= 35 + 3$$
    $$= 38$$

    > I break apart $7\frac{3}{5}$ into 7 and $\frac{3}{5}$. 5 sevens equals 35, and 5 copies of 3 fifths equals 15 fifths, or 3.

3. Amina's dog ate $2\frac{2}{3}$ cups of dog food each day for three weeks. How much dog food did Amina's dog eat during the three weeks?

    > There are 7 days in a week. To find the number of days in 3 weeks, I multiply 7×3. There are 21 days in 3 weeks.

    $$21 \times 2\frac{2}{3} = 42 + \frac{42}{3}$$
    $$= 42 + 14$$
    $$= 56$$

    Amina's dog ate 56 cups of food during the three weeks.

EUREKA MATH™   **Lesson 38:**   Find the product of a whole number and a mixed number using the distributive property.   **55**

©2015 Great Minds. eureka-math.org
G4-M1-HWH-1.3.0-07.2015

G4-M5-Lesson 39

1. It takes $9\frac{2}{3}$ yards of yarn to make one baby blanket. Upik needs four times as much yarn to make four baby blankets. She already has 6 yards of yarn. How many more yards of yarn does Upik need to buy in order to make four baby blankets?

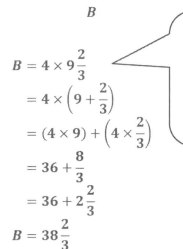

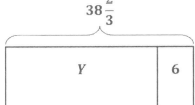

$$B = 4 \times 9\frac{2}{3}$$

I multiply to solve for how many total yards of yarn it takes to make four baby blankets.

$$= 4 \times \left(9 + \frac{2}{3}\right)$$

$$= (4 \times 9) + \left(4 \times \frac{2}{3}\right)$$

$$= 36 + \frac{8}{3}$$

$$= 36 + 2\frac{2}{3}$$

$$B = 38\frac{2}{3}$$

$$Y = 38\frac{2}{3} - 6$$

I subtract 6 yards of yarn that Upik already has.

$$= 32\frac{2}{3}$$

Upik needs to buy $32\frac{2}{3}$ more yards of yarn.

EUREKA MATH

2. The caterpillar crawled $34\frac{2}{3}$ centimeters on Monday. He crawled 5 times as far on Tuesday. How far did he crawl in the two days?

> I use the tape diagram to find the most efficient way to solve. To solve for C, I find the value of 6 units.

Monday | 34 | $\frac{2}{3}$

Tuesday | 34 | $\frac{2}{3}$ | 34 | $\frac{2}{3}$ | 34 | $\frac{2}{3}$ | 34 | $\frac{2}{3}$ | 34 | $\frac{2}{3}$

$\bigg\}\,C$

The caterpillar crawled 208 centimeters, or 2 meters 8 centimeters, on Monday and Tuesday.

$$C = 6 \times 34\frac{2}{3}$$

$$C = (6 \times 34) + \left(6 \times \frac{2}{3}\right)$$

$$C = 204 + \frac{12}{3}$$

$$C = 204 + 4$$

$$C = 208$$

G4-M5-Lesson 40

Noura recorded the growth of her plant during the year.

The measurements are listed in the table.

1. Use the data to create a line plot.

> I remember making a line plot in Lesson 28.

Growth of Plant

Inches

x = growth in one month

2. How many inches did Noura's plant grow in the spring months of March, April, and May?

N

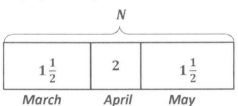

$1\frac{1}{2}$	2	$1\frac{1}{2}$
March	*April*	*May*

> I add the whole numbers first!

$N = 1\frac{1}{2} + 1 + 1\frac{1}{2}$

$N = 3 + \frac{2}{2}$

$N = 4$

Noura's plant grew a total of 4 inches during the spring months.

3. In which months did her plant grow twice as many inches as it did in October?

T

$\frac{3}{4}$	$\frac{3}{4}$

> I use multiplication to solve!

$T = 2 \times \dfrac{3}{4}$

$T = \dfrac{6}{4}$

$T = 1\dfrac{1}{2}$

> I can use a number bond or number line to help rename a fraction to a mixed number, if needed.

Noura's plant grew twice as many inches in the months of May and March as it did in October.

Month	Growth of Plant (in inches)
January	$\frac{1}{2}$
February	$\frac{3}{4}$
March	$1\frac{1}{2}$
April	2
May	$1\frac{1}{2}$
June	$1\frac{3}{4}$
July	$2\frac{3}{4}$
August	$2\frac{1}{4}$
September	1
October	$\frac{3}{4}$
November	$\frac{1}{2}$
December	$\frac{1}{4}$

EUREKA MATH

G4-M5-Lesson 41

1. Find the sums.

> I draw brackets connecting fractions that add up to equal 1.

> There are 2 pairs of fractions that equal 1. 2 fourths is leftover without a partner.

a. $\dfrac{0}{3} + \dfrac{1}{3} + \dfrac{2}{3} + \dfrac{3}{3}$

$$\left(\dfrac{0}{3} + \dfrac{3}{3}\right) + \left(\dfrac{1}{3} + \dfrac{2}{3}\right) = 1 + 1 = 2$$

> The denominator is odd. Every addend has a partner.

b. $\dfrac{0}{4} + \dfrac{1}{4} + \dfrac{2}{4} + \dfrac{3}{4} + \dfrac{4}{4}$

$$\left(\dfrac{0}{4} + \dfrac{4}{4}\right) + \left(\dfrac{1}{4} + \dfrac{3}{4}\right) + \dfrac{2}{4} = 1 + 1 + \dfrac{1}{2} = 2\dfrac{1}{2}$$

> The denominator is even. One addend does not have a partner. This could be a pattern.

2. Find the sums.

> I notice patterns that help me solve without calculating!

a. $\dfrac{0}{13} + \dfrac{1}{13} + \dfrac{2}{13} + \cdots + \dfrac{13}{13}$

     7

> I think about the number of addends, 14, in the expression with odd denominators.

b. $\dfrac{0}{16} + \dfrac{1}{16} + \dfrac{2}{16} + \cdots + \dfrac{16}{16}$

     $8\dfrac{8}{16}$

> There are 17 addends in this expression with even denominators. Half of 17 is $8\dfrac{1}{2}$.

3. How can you apply this strategy to find the sum of all the whole numbers from 0 to 1,000?

Sample Student Response:

I can pair the $1,001$ addends from 0 to $1,000$ to make sums that equal $1,000$. There would be 500 pairs. One addend would be left over. I multiply $1,000 \times 500$, which makes $500,000$. When I add the left over addend, I have a total sum of $500,500$.

EUREKA MATH   **Lesson 41:**   Find and use a pattern to calculate the sum of all fractional parts between 0 and 1. Share and critique peer strategies.   **59**

©2015 Great Minds. eureka-math.org
G4-M1-HWH-1.3.0-07.2015

Grade 4
Module 6

G4-M6-Lesson 1

1. Shade the bottle to show the correct amount. Write the total amount of water in fraction form.

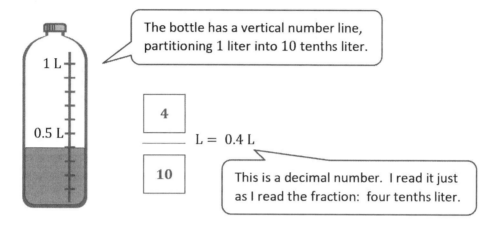

The bottle has a vertical number line, partitioning 1 liter into 10 tenths liter.

$\frac{4}{10}$ L = 0.4 L

This is a decimal number. I read it just as I read the fraction: four tenths liter.

2. Write the weight of the pineapple on the scale in fraction form.

I can read the weight of the pineapple two ways: zero point nine kilograms or nine tenths kilogram.

$\frac{9}{10}$ kg

3. Fill in the blank to make the sentence true in both fraction form and decimal form.

$\frac{3}{10}$ cm + $\frac{7}{10}$ cm = 1 cm   0.3 cm + 0.7 cm = 1.0 cm

$\frac{10}{10}$ cm is equal to 1 cm.

To find pairs of tenths that make 1.0 cm, I think of partners to 10, like 3 and 7, and 9 and 1.

EUREKA
MATH™

Lesson 1:   Use metric measurement to model the decomposition of one whole into tenths.

1

©2015 Great Minds. eureka-math.org
G4-M1-HWH-1.3.0-07.2015

G4-M6-Lesson 2

1. For the length given below, draw a line segment to match. Express the measurement as an equivalent mixed number.

    2.7 cm

    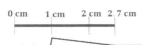

    $2.7 \text{ cm} = 2\frac{7}{10} \text{ cm}$

    > I can express a decimal as a mixed number. The decimal and fractional part for this number have the unit *tenths*.

    > I draw a 2 cm line, then extend it $\frac{7}{10}$ cm.

2. Write the following in decimal form. Then, model and rename the number.

    a. 1 one and 7 tenths = __1.7__

    > Each rectangle represents 1. There are 10 tenths in 1.

    > I shade 17 tenths to show 1.7.

    $1\frac{7}{10} = 1 + \frac{7}{10} = 1 + 0.7 = 1.7$

    b. $\frac{22}{10} =$ __2.2__

    > There are 5 rectangles representing 5 ones in all.

    > I use a number bond to decompose the whole and the fraction. 20 tenths is equal to 2 ones.

    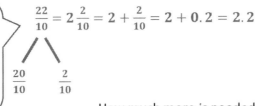

    $\frac{22}{10} = 2\frac{2}{10} = 2 + \frac{2}{10} = 2 + 0.2 = 2.2$

    $\frac{20}{10}$ $\frac{2}{10}$

    How much more is needed to get to 5? __2 ones 8 tenths__

EUREKA MATH

©2015 Great Minds. eureka-math.org
G4-M1-HWH-1.3.0-07.2015

G4-M6-Lesson 3

1. Circle groups of tenths to make as many ones as possible.

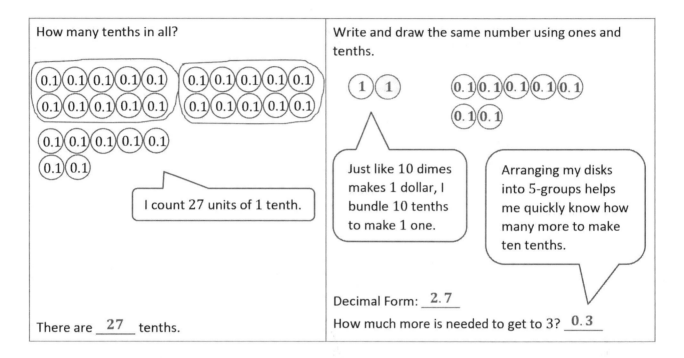

2. Draw disks to represent 2 tens 3 ones 5 tenths using tens, ones, and tenths. Then, show the expanded form of the number in fraction form and decimal form.

$$(2 \times 10) + (3 \times 1) + \left(5 \times \frac{1}{10}\right) = 23\frac{5}{10}$$

I write a multiplication expression for the value of each digit in $23\frac{5}{10}$.

$$(2 \times 10) + (3 \times 1) + (5 \times 0.1) = 23.5$$

I can write in decimal form. Zero point one is another way to write 1 tenth.

EUREKA MATH   **Lesson 3:**   Represent mixed numbers with units of tens, ones, and tenths with   3
number disks, on the number line, and in expanded form.

©2015 Great Minds. eureka-math.org
G4-M1-HWH-1.3.0-07.2015

3. Complete the chart.

Number Line	Decimal Form	Mixed Number (ones and fraction form)	Expanded Form (fraction or decimal form)	How much to get to the next one?
19 ──────── 20	19.3	$19\frac{3}{10}$	$(1 \times 10) + (9 \times 1) + \left(3 \times \frac{1}{10}\right)$	$\frac{7}{10}$

The number line is partitioned into 10 equal parts. To find the endpoints, I ask myself, "Between what two whole numbers is $19\frac{3}{10}$?"

Lesson 3:   Represent mixed numbers with units of tens, ones, and tenths with
                            number disks, on the number line, and in expanded form.

EUREKA
MATH

G4-M6-Lesson 4

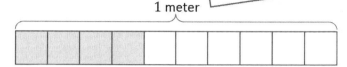

1 meter equals 100 centimeters. When a meter is decomposed into 10 equal parts, 1 part equals $\frac{1}{10}$ meter or 10 centimeters.

1.

   a. What is the length of the shaded part of the meter stick in centimeters?

   40 centimeters

   b. What fraction of a meter is 4 centimeters?

   $\frac{4}{100}$ meter

Each tenth of a meter would need to be decomposed into 10 equal parts to show all 100 centimeters in 1 meter. To represent 4 centimeters, I would shade 4 of the 100 parts.

   c. What fraction of a meter is 40 centimeters?

   $\frac{4}{10}$ meter or $\frac{40}{100}$ meter

2. Fill in the blank.

   $$\frac{3}{10}\text{ m} = \frac{30}{100}\text{ m}$$

1 out of 100 centimeters is 1 hundredth centimeter.

3. On the meter stick, shade in the amount shown. Then, write the equivalent decimal.

   $$\frac{51}{100}\text{ m} = 0.51\text{ m}$$

   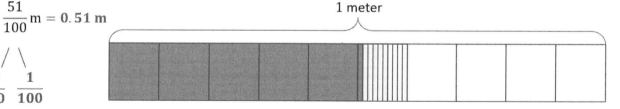

   I shade 5 tenths of a meter. After partitioning the next tenth meter into 10 equal parts, I shade 1 hundredth meter more.

4. Draw a number bond, pulling out the tenths from the hundredths. Write the total as the equivalent decimal.

   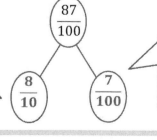

   0.87

   8 tenths is the same as 80 hundredths.

   I can decompose a fraction like I decompose a whole number. I break 87 hundredths into 80 hundredths and 7 hundredths.

EUREKA MATH™   Lesson 4:   Use meters to model the decomposition of one whole into hundredths.   5
                             Represent and count hundredths.

©2015 Great Minds. eureka-math.org
G4-M1-HWH-1.3.0-07.2015

G4-M6-Lesson 5

1. Find the equivalent fraction using multiplication or division. Shade the area models to show the equivalency. Record it as a decimal.

a. $\dfrac{1 \times 10}{10 \times 10} = \dfrac{10}{100}$

> I multiply the number of tenths by 10 to get the number of hundredths.

b. $\dfrac{70 \div 10}{100 \div 10} = \dfrac{7}{10}$

> I divide the number of hundredths by 10 to get the number of tenths.

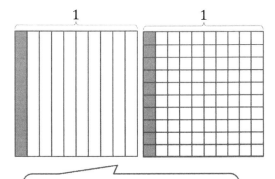

> There are 10 times as many hundredths as there are tenths.

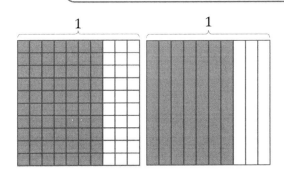

> $\dfrac{7}{10}$ and $\dfrac{70}{100}$ are equivalent fractions.

2. Complete the number sentence. Shade the equivalent amount on the area model, drawing horizontal lines to make hundredths.

a. 25 hundredths = __2__ tenths + __5__ hundredths

b. Decimal Form: __0.25__

c. Fraction Form: $\dfrac{25}{100}$

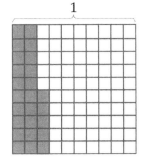

Lesson 5:   Model the equivalence of tenths and hundredths using the area model and number disks.

EUREKA
MATH

3. Circle hundredths to compose as many tenths as you can. Complete the number sentence. Represent the composition with a number bond.

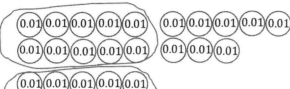

I compose 10 hundredths to make 1 tenth because $\frac{1}{10} = \frac{10}{100}$.

__28__ hundredths = __2__ tenths + __8__ hundredths

4. Use both tenths and hundredths place value disks to represent each number. Write the equivalent number in decimal, fraction, and unit form.

a. $\frac{54}{100} = 0.54$

⓪.1 ⓪.1 ⓪.1 ⓪.1 ⓪.1   ⓪.01 ⓪.01 ⓪.01 ⓪.01

__54__ hundredths

b. $\frac{60}{100} = 0.60$

⓪.1 ⓪.1 ⓪.1 ⓪.1 ⓪.1
⓪.1

60 hundredths

Since I know that $\frac{6}{10} = \frac{60}{100}$, it is more efficient to show 6 tenths than 60 hundredths.

EUREKA MATH   **Lesson 5:** Model the equivalence of tenths and hundredths using the area model and number disks.   **7**

©2015 Great Minds. eureka-math.org
G4-M1-HWH-1.3.0-07.2015

G4-M6-Lesson 6

1. Shade the area models to represent the number, drawing horizontal lines to make hundredths as needed. Locate the corresponding point on the number line. Label with a point, and record the mixed number as a decimal.

$3\frac{42}{100} = \underline{3.42}$

> There are 3 ones in $3\frac{42}{100}$. I shade 3 area models completely.

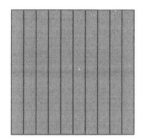 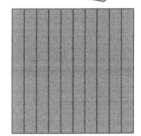  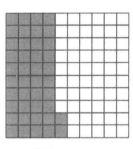

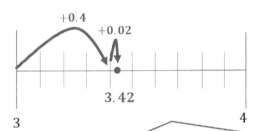

> I shade 42 hundredths after drawing horizontal lines to decompose tenths into hundredths.

> To find 3.42 on the number line, I begin with the largest unit. I start at 3 ones. I slide 4 tenths. Then, I estimate where 2 hundredths would be.

2. Write the equivalent fraction and decimal for the following number.

    9 ones 7 hundredths

    $9\frac{7}{100}$ 9.07

> There are no tenths in this number! I show that with a zero as a placeholder.

> To write a decimal number, I place a decimal point between the ones and the fraction.

EUREKA
MATH

G4-M6-Lesson 7

1. Write a decimal number sentence to identify the total value of the place value disks.

(10)(10)	(1)	(0.1)(0.1)(0.1)(0.1)(0.1)	(0.01)(0.01)(0.01)(0.01)
2 tens	1 one	5 tenths	4 hundredths

$$\underline{\quad 20 \quad} + \underline{\quad 1 \quad} + \underline{\quad 0.5 \quad} + \underline{\quad 0.04 \quad} = \underline{\quad 21.54 \quad}$$

> I write the expanded form.

2. Use the place value chart to answer the following questions. Express the value of the digit in unit form.

hundreds	tens	ones	.	tenths	hundredths
3	5	1	.	8	2

a. The digit __3__ is in the hundreds place. It has a value of __3 hundreds__.

> I write the value of 300 in unit form.

b. The digit __5__ is in the tens place. It has a value of __5 tens__.

3. Write the decimal as an equivalent fraction. Then, write the number in expanded form, using both decimal and fraction notation.

Decimal and Fraction Form	Expanded Form	
	Fraction Notation	**Decimal Notation**
$27.03 = 27\dfrac{3}{100}$	$(2 \times 10) + (7 \times 1) + \left(3 \times \dfrac{1}{100}\right)$ $20 + 7 + \dfrac{3}{100}$	$(2 \times 10) + (7 \times 1) + (3 \times 0.01)$ $20 + 7 + 0.03$
$400.80 = 400\dfrac{80}{100}$	$(4 \times 100) + \left(8 \times \dfrac{1}{10}\right)$ $400 + \dfrac{8}{10}$	$(4 \times 100) + (8 \times 0.1)$ $400 + 0.8$

> This number has many zeros! There are values in the hundreds and tenths place that I show as addends in the expressions.

> Expanded form can be written two ways. Using parentheses, I show how the value of each digit is a multiple of a base-ten unit (e.g., 4×100). Or, I show the value of each digit (e.g., 400).

EUREKA MATH
Lesson 7: Model mixed numbers with units of hundreds, tens, ones, tenths, and hundredths in expanded form and on the place value chart.   9

©2015 Great Minds. eureka-math.org
G4-M1-HWH-1.3.0-07.2015

G4-M6-Lesson 8

1. Use the area model to represent $\frac{140}{100}$. Complete the number sentence.

    $\frac{140}{100} = \underline{\ 14\ }$ tenths $= \underline{\ 1\ }$ one $\underline{\ 4\ }$ tenths $= \underline{\ 1.4\ }$

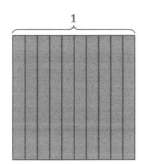 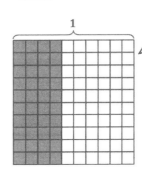

I can draw horizontal lines to show hundredths. 1 one equals 10 tenths or 100 hundredths. 4 tenths equals 40 hundredths.

I shade 14 tenths. My model shows that 14 tenths is the same as 1 one and 4 tenths.

2. Draw place value disks to represent the following decomposition:

    2 tenths 3 hundredths $= \underline{\ 23\ }$ hundredths

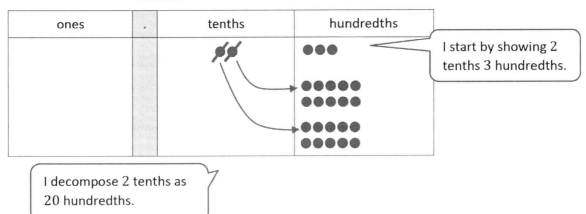

I start by showing 2 tenths 3 hundredths.

I decompose 2 tenths as 20 hundredths.

Lesson 8:   Use understanding of fraction equivalence to investigate decimal
                          numbers on the place value chart expressed in different units.

EUREKA
MATH

3. Decompose the units to represent each number as tenths.

   a.   1.3 = __13__ tenths   b.   18.3 = __183__ tenths

4. Decompose the units to represent each number as hundredths.

   a.   1.3 = __130__ hundredths   b.   18.3 = __1,830__ hundredths

   > I notice a pattern! There are 10 times as many hundredths as tenths.

5. Complete the chart.

Decimal	Mixed Number	Tenths	Hundredths
8.2	$8\frac{2}{10}$	82 *tenths* $\frac{82}{10}$	820 *hundredths* $\frac{820}{100}$

   > I write tenths and hundredths in both fraction and unit form.

EUREKA
MATH

Lesson 8:   Use understanding of fraction equivalence to investigate decimal
                 numbers on the place value chart expressed in different units.

11

©2015 Great Minds. eureka-math.org
G4-M1-HWH-1.3.0-07.2015

G4-M6-Lesson 9

1. Express the lengths of the shaded parts in decimal form. Write a sentence that compares the two lengths. Use the expression *shorter than* or *longer than* in your sentence.

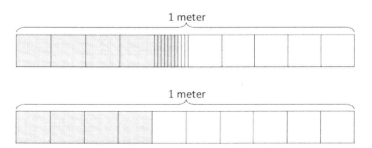

1 meter

0.47

> I know that $0.47 = 4$ tenths 7 hundredths.

1 meter

0.4

> I know that $0.4 = 4$ tenths.

0.47 meter is longer than 0.4 meter.

> Both numbers have 4 tenths. 0.47 meter is longer because it has an additional 7 hundredths. I can see that by looking at the tape diagrams.

2. Examine the mass of each item as shown below on the 1-kilogram scales. Put an X over the items that are lighter than the bananas.

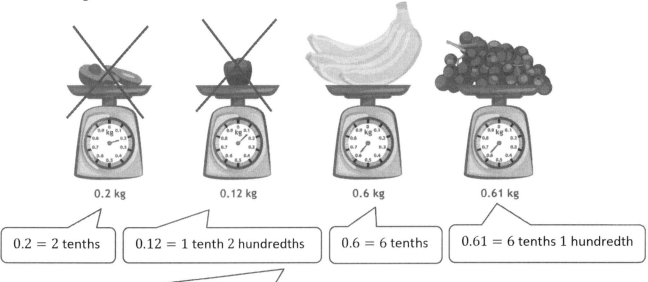

0.2 kg   0.12 kg   0.6 kg   0.61 kg

> 0.2 = 2 tenths

> 0.12 = 1 tenth 2 hundredths

> 0.6 = 6 tenths

> 0.61 = 6 tenths 1 hundredth

> I compare by looking at the largest place value unit in the mass of each item. The largest unit in each item is tenths. The avocado and the apple have fewer tenths than the bananas. The grapes have the same number of tenths, but they also have 1 more hundredth. The grapes are heavier than the bananas.

Lesson 9:   Use the place value chart and metric measurement to compare decimals and answer comparison questions.

3. Record the volume of water in each graduated cylinder on the place value chart below.

 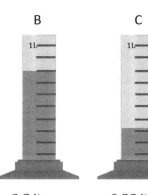

Volume of Water (in liters)

Cylinder	ones	.	tenths	hundredths
A	0	.	7	4
B	0	.	8	0
C	0	.	3	2

0.74 liter   0.8 liter   0.32 liter

Compare the values using >, <, or =.

a.   0.74 L ___>___ 0.32 L

b.   0.32 L ___<___ 0.8 L

c.   0.8 L ___>___ 0.74 L

> I look at the pictures and the completed table to help me compare the values. Tenths are the largest unit in each number, so I can compare the number of tenths in each number to determine which is greater and which is less.

d.   Write the volume of water in each graduated cylinder in order from least to greatest.

   0.32 L,   0.74 L,   0.8 L

EUREKA MATH™   **Lesson 9:**   Use the place value chart and metric measurement to compare decimals and answer comparison questions.   13

©2015 Great Minds. eureka-math.org
G4-M1-HWH-1.3.0-07.2015

G4-M6-Lesson 10

1. Shade the area models below, decomposing tenths as needed, to represent the pair of decimal numbers. Fill in the blank with <, >, or = to compare the decimal numbers.

    0.4 __>__ 0.37

    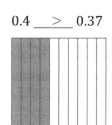 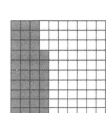

    At first, I thought, "37 is greater than 4." But then I remembered the units of these numbers must be the same in order to compare.
    4 tenths is equal to 40 hundredths, and 40 hundredths is greater than 37 hundredths.

2. Locate and label the points for each of the decimal numbers on the number line. Fill in the blank with <, >, or = to compare the decimal numbers.

    11.02 __<__ 11.21

    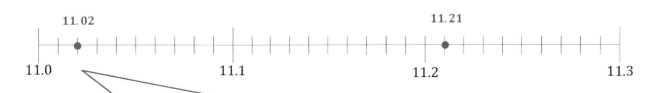

    Each tick mark represents 1 hundredth. 11.0 equals 11 and 0 hundredths. 11.02 equals 11 and 2 hundredths. 11.21 equals 11 and 21 hundredths. I use this information to help me to locate and label the points.

3. Use the symbols <, >, or = to compare.

    1.7 __>__ 1.17

    I know that 1.7 is greater than 1.17 because 1.7 = 1.70 and 1.70 > 1.17.

4. Use the symbols <, >, or = to compare. Use a picture as needed to solve.

    47 tenths __>__ 4.6

    I rename 47 tenths as 4 and 7 tenths. 4.7 > 4.6

Lesson 10:   Use area models and the number line to compare decimal numbers, and record comparisons using <, >, and =.

EUREKA MATH™

©2015 Great Minds. eureka-math.org
G4-M1-HWH-1.3.0-07.2015

G4-M6-Lesson 11

1. Plot the following points on the number line.

1.56, $1\frac{6}{10}$, $\frac{163}{100}$, $\frac{17}{10}$, 1.62, 1 one and 75 hundredths

> I rename all of the numbers to fractions with like units—hundredths. I know that each tick mark represents 1 hundredth.

$1\frac{56}{100}$ $1\frac{60}{100}$ $1\frac{63}{100}$ $1\frac{70}{100}$ $1\frac{62}{100}$ $1\frac{75}{100}$

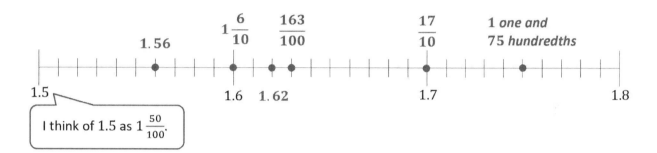

> I think of 1.5 as $1\frac{50}{100}$.

2. Arrange the following numbers in order from greatest to least using decimal form. Use the > symbol between each number.

7 ones and 23 hundredths, $\frac{725}{100}$, 7.4, $7\frac{52}{100}$, $8\frac{2}{10}$, $7\frac{4}{100}$

> I rename all of the numbers to decimal form. To help me order the numbers, I think of $8\frac{2}{10}$ as 8.20 and 7.4 as 7.40.

$8.2 > 7.52 > 7.4 > 7.25 > 7.23 > 7.04$

3. In a frog-jumping contest, Mary's frog jumped 1.04 meters. Kelly's frog jumped 1.4 meters, and Katrina's frog jumped 1.14 meters. Whose frog jumped the farthest distance? Whose frog jumped the shortest distance?

| Mary's Frog | 1.04 m |

> I rename 1.4 to 1.40 to be able to compare hundredths.

| Kelly's Frog | 1.40 m |

Kelly's frog jumped the farthest distance. Mary's frog jumped the shortest distance. I know because they all jumped at least 1 meter, but Kelly's frog jumped an additional 40 hundredths meter, and Mary's frog only jumped an additional 4 hundredths meter.

| Katrina's Frog | 1.14 m |

G4-M6-Lesson 12

1. Complete the number sentence by expressing each part using hundredths. Model using the place value chart.

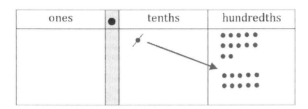

ones	tenths	hundredths

1 tenth + 12 hundredths = __22__ hundredths

10 *hundredths* + 12 *hundredths* = 22 *hundredths*

> To make like units, I change 1 tenth to 10 hundredths.
> 10 hundredths + 12 hundredths = 22 hundredths.

2. Solve by converting all addends to hundredths before solving.

   a. 6 tenths + 21 hundredths = __60__ hundredths + __21__ hundredths = __81__ hundredths

   > This is just like Problem 1. Instead of drawing place value disks, I change the tenths to hundredths in my mind. Each tenth equals 10 hundredths.

   b. 27 hundredths + 3 tenths = __27__ hundredths + __30__ hundredths = __57__ hundredths

   > I can't add because the units are not alike. I can't add 1 cat plus 2 dogs; I have to rename with like units. I can add 1 animal plus 2 animals.

3. Solve. Write your answer as a decimal.

   a. $\frac{3}{10} + \frac{21}{100}$

   $\frac{30}{100} + \frac{21}{100} = \frac{51}{100} = 0.51$

   b. $\frac{14}{100} + \frac{7}{10}$

   $\frac{14}{100} + \frac{70}{100} = \frac{84}{100} = 0.84$

   > To solve, I make like units of hundredths. I add, and then I change the answer from fraction form to decimal form.

Lesson 12:   Apply understanding of fraction equivalence to add tenths and hundredths.

EUREKA MATH

G4-M6-Lesson 13

Lesson Notes

In Grade 4, students add decimals by first writing the addends in fraction form and then adding the fractions to find the total. This strengthens student understanding of the fraction and decimal relationship, increases their ability to think flexibly, and prepares them for greater success with fractions and decimals in Grade 5.

1. Solve. Convert tenths to hundredths before finding the sum. Rewrite the complete number sentence in decimal form.

a. $2\frac{31}{100} + \frac{4}{10}$

> I convert 4 tenths to 40 hundredths.
> I add like units.

$$2\frac{31}{100} + \frac{4}{10} = 2\frac{31}{100} + \frac{40}{100} = 2\frac{71}{100}$$

> Decimal form is another way to express the numbers.

$$2.31 + 0.40 = 2.71$$

b. $4\frac{42}{100} + 2\frac{7}{10}$

> I add ones to ones and hundredths to hundredths.

$$4\frac{42}{100} + 2\frac{7}{10} = 4\frac{42}{100} + 2\frac{70}{100} = 6\frac{112}{100} = 7\frac{12}{100}$$

$$1 \quad \overset{\displaystyle\wedge}{} \quad \frac{12}{100}$$

> I use a number bond to show $\frac{112}{100} = 1 + \frac{12}{100}$ since $\frac{100}{100} = 1$.

$$4.42 + 2.70 = 7.12$$

2. Solve by rewriting the expression in fraction form. After solving, rewrite the complete number sentence in decimal form.

$4.4 + 1.74$

$$4\frac{4}{10} + 1\frac{74}{100} = 4\frac{40}{100} + 1\frac{74}{100} = 5\frac{114}{100} = 6\frac{14}{100}$$

> To add decimal numbers, I solve by relating this problem to adding fractions.

$$1 \quad \overset{\displaystyle\wedge}{} \quad \frac{14}{100}$$

$$4.4 + 1.74 = 6.14$$

G4-M6-Lesson 14

1. At the beginning of 2014, Jordan's height was 1.3 meters. If Jordan grew a total of 0.04 meter in 2014, what was his height at the end of the year?

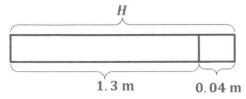

$$H = 1.3 \text{ m} + 0.04 \text{ m}$$
$$= 1\frac{30}{100} \text{ m} + \frac{4}{100} \text{ m}$$
$$= 1\frac{34}{100} \text{ m}$$
$$= 1.34 \text{ m}$$

Jordan's height at the end of the year was 1.34 meters.

> The tape diagram helps me to see that I need to add to solve for H, Jordan's height at the end of the year. I write the decimal numbers in fraction form using like units and then solve.

2. Tyler finished the math problem in 20.74 seconds. He beat his mom's time by 10.03 seconds. What was their combined time?

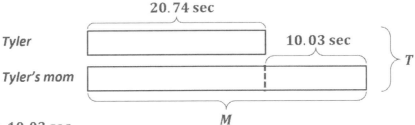

$$T = 20.74 \text{ sec} + 20.74 \text{ sec} + 10.03 \text{ sec}$$
$$= 20\frac{74}{100} \text{ sec} + 20\frac{74}{100} \text{ sec} + 10\frac{3}{100} \text{ sec}$$
$$= 50\frac{151}{100} \text{ sec}$$

1 sec $\frac{51}{100}$ sec

$$= 51\frac{51}{100} \text{ sec}$$
$$T = 51.51 \text{ sec}$$

Their combined time was 51.51 seconds.

EUREKA
MATH™

G4-M6-Lesson 15

Lesson Notes

In Grade 4, students find the sum of money amounts by expressing the amounts in unit form, adding like units (i.e., dollars + dollars and cents + cents), and then writing the answer in decimal form with a dollar sign. Writing money amounts in unit form and fraction form builds a strong conceptual foundation for decimal notation. Students are introduced to adding decimal numbers in Grade 5.

1. 4 pennies = $ _0_ . _04_   4¢ = $\frac{4}{100}$ dollar

2. 8 dimes = $ _0_ . _80_   80¢ = $\frac{8}{10}$ dollar

3. 2 quarters = $ _0_ . _50_   50¢ = $\frac{50}{100}$ dollar

> 1 penny = $\frac{1}{100}$ dollar
>
> 1 dime = $\frac{1}{10}$ dollar
>
> 1 quarter = $\frac{25}{100}$ dollar

Solve. Give the total amount of money in fraction and decimal form.

4. 7 dimes and 23 pennies

$$(7 \times 10¢) + (23 \times 1¢) = 70¢ + 23¢ = 93¢$$

$$93¢ = \frac{93}{100} \text{ dollar}$$

$$\frac{93}{100} \text{ dollar} = \$0.93$$

> 93 cents is 93 hundredths of a dollar. Thinking of that value as a fraction helps me to write it as a decimal number.

5. 1 quarter 3 dimes and 6 pennies

$$(1 \times 25¢) + (3 \times 10¢) + (6 \times 1¢) = 25¢ + 30¢ + 6¢ = 61¢$$

$$61¢ = \frac{61}{100} \text{ dollar}$$

$$\frac{61}{100} \text{ dollar} = \$0.61$$

©2015 Great Minds. eureka-math.org
G4-M1-HWH-1.3.0-07.2015

6. 173 cents is what fraction of a dollar?

$\frac{173}{100}$ *dollars*

I know that 1 cent $= \frac{1}{100}$ dollar.

Solve. Express the answer in decimal form.

7. 2 dollars 3 dimes 24 pennies + 3 dollars 1 quarter

2 *dollars* 54 *cents* + 3 *dollars* 25 *cents* = 5 *dollars* 79 *cents*

5 *dollars* 79 *cents* = $5\frac{79}{100}$ *dollars* = \$5.79

I rewrite each addend as dollars and cents. I add like units and then express the amount in decimal form.

8. 7 dollars 5 dimes 2 pennies + 1 dollar 3 quarters

7 *dollars* 52 *cents* + 1 *dollar* 75 *cents* = 8 *dollars* 127 *cents* = 9 *dollars* 27 *cents*

1 *dollar*   27 *cents*

9 *dollars* 27 *cents* = $9\frac{27}{100}$ *dollars* = \$9.27

Lesson 15:   Express money amounts given in various forms as decimal numbers.

EUREKA MATH

G4-M6-Lesson 16

Use the RDW process to solve. Write your answer as a decimal.

1. Soo Jin needs 4 dollars 15 cents to buy a school lunch. At the bottom of her backpack, she finds 2 dollar bills, 5 quarters, and 4 pennies. How much more money does Soo Jin need to buy a school lunch?

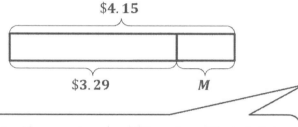

$4.15

$3.29   M

M = 4 dollars 15 cents − 3 dollars 29 cents

= 1 dollar 15 cents − 29 cents

100 cents   15 cents

= 86 cents

= $0.86

Soo Jin needs $0.86 more to buy a school lunch.

Another way to solve 115 cents − 29 cents is to add 1 to each number and then solve 116 − 30. 11 tens 6 ones − 3 tens = 8 tens 6 ones.

2. Kelly has 2 quarters and 3 dimes. Jack has 5 dollars, 4 dimes, and 7 pennies. Emma has 3 dollars, 1 quarter, and 1 dime. They want to put their money together to buy a pizza that costs $11.00. Do they have enough? If not, how much more do they need?

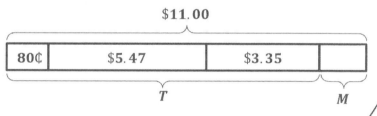

$11.00

| 80¢ | $5.47 | $3.35 | |

T   M

I determine how much money Kelly, Jack, and Emma each have. I add to find out how much money they have together. Then, I subtract that amount from the cost of the pizza to find out how much more money they need, *M*.

T = 80 cents + 5 dollars 47 cents + 3 dollars 35 cents

= 8 dollars 162 cents

1 dollar   62 cents

= 9 dollars 62 cents

Kelly, Jack, and Emma have $9.62.

M = 11 dollars − 9 dollars 62 cents

10 dollars   100 cents

= 1 dollar 38 cents

They do not have enough money to buy the pizza. They need $1.38 more.

3. A pint of ice cream costs $2.49. A box of ice cream cup sundaes costs twice as much as the pint of ice cream. Brandon buys a pint of ice cream and a box of ice cream cup sundaes. How much money does he spend?

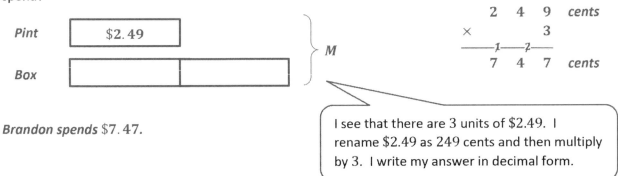

Brandon spends $7.47.

> I see that there are 3 units of $2.49. I rename $2.49 as 249 cents and then multiply by 3. I write my answer in decimal form.

4. Katrina has 3 dollars 28 cents. Gail has 7 dollars 52 cents. How much money does Gail need to give Katrina so that each of them has the same amount of money?

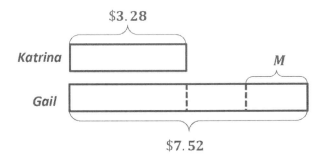

> The tape diagram helps me to solve. I see that if Gail gives Katrina half of the difference, they will have the same amount. I subtract to find the difference, and then I divide by 2.

7 dollars 52 cents − 3 dollars 28 cents = 4 dollars 24 cents

= 424 cents

$$
\begin{array}{r}
2\ \ 1\ \ 2 \\
2\,\overline{)\,4\ \ 2\ \ 4\,} \\
-\ 4 \\
\hline
0\ \ 2 \\
-\ \ \ 2 \\
\hline
0\ \ 4 \\
-\ \ \ 4 \\
\hline
0
\end{array}
$$

212 *cents* = $2.12

M = $2.12

Gail needs to give Katrina $2.12 so that each of them has the same amount of money.

EUREKA
MATH

Homework Helpers

Grade 4
Module 7

G4-M7-Lesson 1

1. Complete the tables.

a.

Yards	Feet
1	3
4	12
10	30

b.

Feet	Inches
1	12
3	36
9	108

c.

Yards	Inches
1	36
2	72
4	144

1 yard = 3 feet. I multiply the number of yards by 3 to find the number of feet.

1 foot = 12 inches. I multiply the number of feet by 12 to find the number of inches.

1 yard = 3 feet, and 1 foot = 12 inches. To find the number of inches in 1 yard, I can multiply, $3 \times 12 = 36$. Now I multiply the number of yards by 36 to find the number of inches.

2. Solve.

a. 3 yards 2 inches = ___**110**___ inches

There are 36 inches in 1 yard. 3×36 inches = 108 inches.

b. 12 yards 4 feet = ___**40**___ feet

There are 3 feet in 1 yard. 12×3 feet = 36 feet.

c. 3 yards 1 foot = ___**120**___ inches

I can solve this two ways: Convert yards and feet to inches, or convert yards to feet and then feet to inches.

Lesson 1: Create conversion tables for length, weight, and capacity units using measurement tools, and use the tables to solve problems.

1

EUREKA MATH™

3. Complete the table.

Pounds	Ounces
1	16
3	48
5	80

> 1 pound = 16 ounces. I multiply the number of pounds by 16 to find the number of ounces.

4. Ronald's cat weighs 9 pounds 3 ounces. How many ounces does his cat weigh?

9 pounds 3 ounces

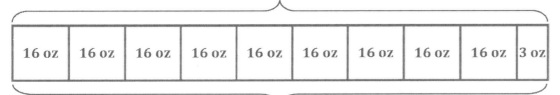

| 16 oz | 16 oz | 16 oz | 16 oz | 16 oz | 16 oz | 16 oz | 16 oz | 16 oz | 3 oz |

T

1 *unit: 16 ounces*

9 *units: 144 ounces*

T = 144 *ounces* + 3 *ounces*

T = 147 *ounces*

Ronald's cat weighs 147 *ounces.*

$$\begin{array}{r} 1\ 6 \\ \times\quad\ 9 \\ \hline 1\ 4\ 4 \end{array}$$

> I can draw a tape diagram with 9 units of 16 ounces and 1 unit of 3 ounces because the cat weighs 9 pounds 3 ounces and each pound equals 16 ounces.

> I can multiply 9 × 16 to find the number of ounces in 9 pounds. Then I can add 3 more ounces to find the total number of ounces.

5. Answer *true* or *false* for the following statement. If the statement is false, change the right side of the comparison to make it true.

2 kilograms < 1,900 grams   _*false*_

2,001 grams

> The statement is false because 2,000 grams is not less than 1,900 grams. The number on the right has to be greater than 2,000.

1 kilogram = 1,000 grams

2 × 1,000 grams = 2,000 grams

2 kilograms = 2,000 grams

Lesson 1:   Create conversion tables for length, weight, and capacity units using measurement tools, and use the tables to solve problems.

EUREKA MATH™

G4-M7-Lesson 2

Use the RDW process to solve Problems 1 and 2.

1. Lucy buys 2 gallons of milk. How many cups of milk does she have?

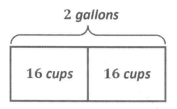

2 gallons

| 16 cups | 16 cups |

> I can draw a tape diagram with 2 units of 16 cups because Lucy bought 2 gallons of milk and each gallon is the same as 16 cups.

1 unit: **16 cups**

2 units: 2×16 **cups = 32 cups**

Lucy has 32 cups of milk.

> I multiply 2×16 cups to find the number of cups in 2 gallons.

2. Matthew drank 2 liters of water today, which was 320 milliliters more water than Sarah drank today. How much water did Sarah drink today?

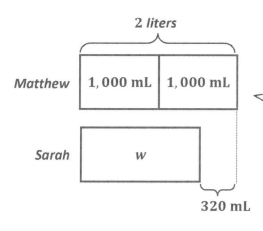

2 liters

Matthew | 1,000 mL | 1,000 mL

Sarah | w

320 mL

> I draw tape diagrams to represent the amount of water Matthew and Sarah drank. Matthew's tape diagram is longer than Sarah's because he drank 320 more milliliters of water than she did.

$1 \text{ L} = 1,000 \text{ mL}$

$2 \text{ L} = 2,000 \text{ mL}$

$w = 2,000 \text{ mL} - 320 \text{ mL}$

$w = 1,680 \text{ mL}$

Sarah drank 1,680 mL of water today.

> I convert the amount of water Matthew drank, 2 liters, into milliliters. Then, I subtract from 2,000 mL the excess amount of water that Matthew drank, which is 320 mL. This tells me how much water Sarah drank.

Lesson 2: Create conversion tables for length, weight, and capacity units using measurement tools, and use the tables to solve problems.

3. Complete the tables.

a.

Gallons	Quarts
1	4
3	12
5	20

b.

Quarts	Pints
1	2
4	8
8	16

1 gallon = 4 quarts. I multiply the number of gallons by 4 to find the number of quarts.

1 quart = 2 pints. I multiply the number of quarts by 2 to find the number of pints.

4. Solve.

a. 5 gallons 3 quarts = ___23___ quarts

There are 4 quarts in 1 gallon.
5 × 4 quarts = 20 quarts.

b. 25 gallons 2 quarts = ___408___   cups

I can solve this two ways: Convert gallons and quarts to cups, or convert gallons to quarts and then all quarts to cups.

5. Answer *true* or *false* for the following statement. If your answer is false, make the statement true by correcting the right side of the comparison.

6 pints > 3 ~~quarts~~ 1 cup   ___*false*___

2 quarts 1 cup

2 pints = 1 quart
3 × 2 pints = 6 pints
3 quarts 1 cup = 6 pints 1 cup

The statement is false because 6 pints is not greater than 6 pints 1 cup. The number on the right has to be less than 3 quarts.

Lesson 2:   Create conversion tables for length, weight, and capacity units using
                            measurement tools, and use the tables to solve problems.

EUREKA
MATH

G4-M7-Lesson 3

Use RDW to solve Problem 1.

1. Benjamin's football practice ends at 5:00 p.m. If practice starts at 3:00 p.m., how many minutes long is practice? Use the number line to show your work.

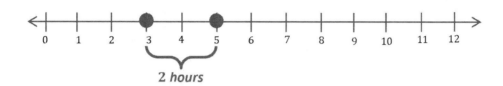

1 *hour* = 60 *minutes*

2 *hours* = 120 *minutes*

> I plot the times on the number line.
> Then, I convert the hours to minutes.

Benjamin's practice lasts for 120 *minutes.*

2. Complete the following conversion tables.

a.

Hours	Minutes
1	60
3	180
6	360

> 1 hour = 60 minutes
> I multiply the number of hours by 60 to find the number of minutes.

b.

Days	Hours
1	24
2	48
4	96

> 1 day = 24 hours
> I multiply the number of days by 24 to find the number of hours.

©2015 Great Minds. eureka-math.org
G4-M1-HWH-1.3.0-07.2015

3. Solve.

a. 9 hours 20 minutes = __560__ minutes

> There are 60 minutes in 1 hour.
> 9×60 minutes = 540 minutes.

b. 5 minutes 45 seconds = __345__ seconds

> There are 60 seconds in 1 minute.
> 5×60 seconds = 300 seconds.

c. 3 days 15 hours = __87__ hours

> There are 24 hours in 1 day.
> 3×24 hours = 72 hours.

4. In the 1860s, it took a steamship about 1 week 2 days to cross the Atlantic Ocean. How many hours are there in 1 week 2 days?

1 week 2 days

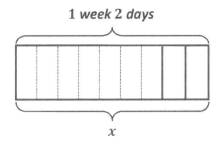

x

> I can draw a tape diagram to represent 1 week 2 days. I know that there are 7 days in 1 week, so 1 week 2 days = 9 days. I can partition my tape diagram into 9 units to represent 9 days.

1 unit: 1 day = 24 hours

9 units: 9×24 hours = 216 hours

x = 216 hours

$$\begin{array}{r} 2\ 4 \\ \times \quad\ 9 \\ \hline 2\ 1\ 6 \end{array}$$

> I can multiply 9×24 to find the total number of hours in 9 days, or 1 week 2 days.

There are 216 hours in 1 week 2 days.

6   Lesson 3:   Create conversion tables for units of time, and use the tables to solve problems.

EUREKA
MATH™

G4-M7-Lesson 4

Use RDW to solve the following problems.

1. Rebecca painted her bathroom in 2 hours. It took her twice as long to paint her kitchen. How many minutes did Rebecca spend painting her bathroom and kitchen?

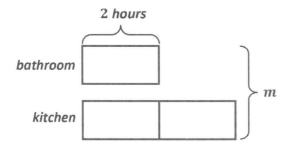

> I draw 1 unit of 2 hours to represent the amount of time Rebecca spends painting her bathroom. I draw 2 units of 2 hours to represent the amount of time she spends painting her kitchen.

1 unit: 2 hours

3 units: 3 × 2 hours = 6 hours

m = 6 × 60 minutes

m = 360 minutes

Rebecca spent 360 minutes painting her bathroom and kitchen.

2. Mason's little sister weighed 7 pounds 9 ounces at birth. At her 6-month check-up, Mason's little sister weighed 16 pounds. How many ounces did Mason's little sister gain?

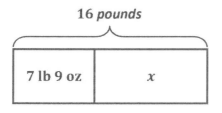

> I draw a tape diagram to represent the problem. I know a part and the whole. I subtract to find the unknown part. Then, I convert 8 pounds to ounces and add 7 more ounces.

16 pounds − 7 pounds 9 ounces = 8 pounds 7 ounces

15 *pounds*   16 *ounces*

x = 8 pounds 7 ounces = (8 × 16 ounces) + 7 ounces = 128 ounces + 7 ounces = 135 ounces

Mason's little sister gained 135 ounces.

3. Melissa stocks 16 quarts of chocolate milk in the refrigerated case at a grocery store. She puts twice as many quarts of whole milk as chocolate milk in the case. Melissa stocks 7 fewer quarts of almond milk than whole milk in the case.

    a. How many quarts of almond milk did Melissa stock in the refrigerated case?

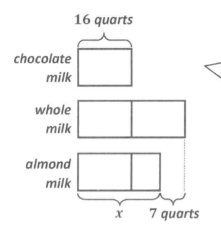

> The tape diagrams show the relationships among the different amounts of each type of milk Melissa stocked. The amount of whole milk is equal to 2 units of chocolate milk. The amount of almond milk is 7 quarts less than the almond milk.

1 unit: 16 *quarts*

2 units: 2×16 *quarts* $= 32$ *quarts*

$x = 32$ *quarts* $- 7$ *quarts*

$x = 25$ *quarts*

> I find the amount of whole milk by doubling the amount of chocolate milk. I find the amount of almond milk by subtracting 7 quarts from the amount of whole milk.

Melissa stocked 25 *quarts of almond milk.*

    b. Is the total number of quarts of chocolate milk, whole milk, and almond milk more than the 18 gallons of skim milk that are in the refrigerated case? Explain your answer.

16 *quarts* $+ 32$ *quarts* $+ 25$ *quarts* $= 73$ *quarts*

18 *gallons* $= 18 \times 4$ *quarts* $= 72$ *quarts*

Yes, the total number of quarts of whole milk, chocolate milk, and almond milk is more than the 18 gallons of skim milk. 18 gallons is the same as 72 quarts, and the total for the other types of milk is 73 quarts. There is 1 fewer quart of skim milk than the other types of milk combined.

Lesson 4:   Solve multiplicative comparison word problems using measurement
                              conversion tables.

**EUREKA
MATH**™

G4-M7-Lesson 5

Draw a tape diagram to solve the following problem.

1. Sandy bought a 3-pound bag of flour. Adriana used 11 ounces of that flour to make cookies. Dave used 4 ounces more of that flour than Adriana to make banana bread. How many ounces of flour were left in Sandy's bag?

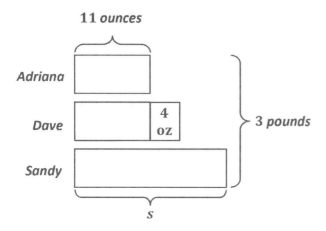

> I can draw tape diagrams to represent the amount of flour Adriana and Dave used and the amount of flour Sandy still has.

$11 \ ounces + 11 \ ounces + 4 \ ounces = 26 \ ounces$

$3 \ pounds = 3 \times 16 \ ounces = 48 \ ounces$

$s = 48 \ ounces - 26 \ ounces$

$s = 22 \ ounces$

Sandy has 22 ounces of flour left.

> After I find the amount of flour Dave and Adriana used, which is 2 units of 11 ounces plus 4 more ounces, I convert 3 pounds to ounces and subtract.

2. Create a problem of your own using the diagram below, and solve for the unknown.

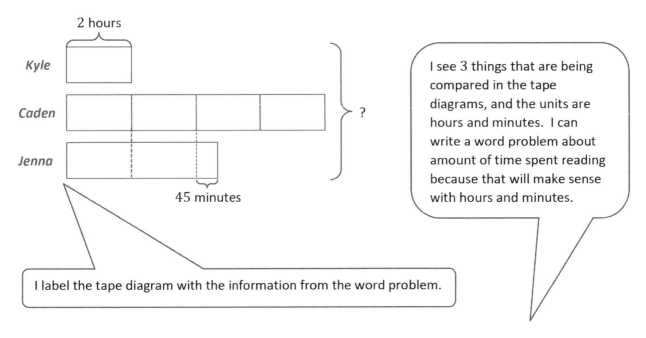

I see 3 things that are being compared in the tape diagrams, and the units are hours and minutes. I can write a word problem about amount of time spent reading because that will make sense with hours and minutes.

I label the tape diagram with the information from the word problem.

Kyle read for 2 hours last week. Caden read four times as long as Kyle read last week. Jenna read 45 minutes more than half the time that Caden read. What is the total number of minutes they read last week?

7×2 *hours* $= 14$ *hours*

14 *hours* 45 *minutes* $= (14 \times 60$ *minutes*$) + 45$ *minutes* $= 840$ *minutes* $+ 45$ *minutes* $= 885$ *minutes*

Kyle, Caden, and Jenna read for a total of 885 minutes last week.

The tape diagrams show 7 units of 2 hours plus 45 minutes, which is equal to 14 hours 45 minutes. I multiply 14×60 to convert the hours to minutes. Then, I add 45 minutes to find the total number of minutes, 885 minutes.

EUREKA
MATH

G4-M7-Lesson 6

> 1 gal = 8 pt
> 1 gal = 4 qt
> 1 qt = 2 pt
> 1 pt = 2 c

1. Determine the following sums and differences. Show your work.

   a. 2 gal 3 qt + 2 qt = __3__ gal __1__ qt

   1 qt 1 qt

   > I decompose and rename units to help me solve. Then, I add or subtract like units.

   b. 5 qt − 3 pt = __3__ qt __1__ pt   3 pt $\xrightarrow{+1\ pt}$ 2 qt $\xrightarrow{+3\ qt}$ 5 qt

   1 qt 1 pt

   > I use the arrow way counting up to 5 quarts from 3 pints. I rename 3 pints as 1 quart 1 pint and then add on 1 pint to reach 2 quarts. Finally, I add on 3 quarts to reach 5 quarts. The answer is the sum of what was added on.

   c. 7 gal 1 pt − 2 pt = __6__ gal __7__ pt

   6 gal 9 pt

   > I rename 1 gallon as 8 pints.

   d. 2 qt 3 c + 3 c = __3__ qt __2__ c   2 qt 3 c + 3 c = 2 qt 6 c = 3 qt 2 c

   1 qt 2 c

2. The capacity of the container is 4 gallons 2 quarts of liquid. Right now, 1 gallon 3 quarts of liquid are in the container. How much more liquid will the container hold?

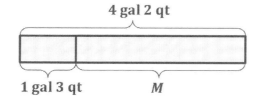

4 gal 2 qt

1 gal 3 qt   M

4 gal 2 qt − 1 gal 3 qt = 2 gal 3 qt

3 gal 6 qt

M = 2 gal 3 qt

The container will hold 2 gallons 3 quarts more liquid.

> I rename 4 gallons 2 quarts as 3 gallons 6 quarts so that there are enough quarts to subtract 3 quarts.

3. Grant and Emma follow the recipe in the table to make punch.

    a.   How much punch does the recipe make?

Punch Recipe	
Ingredient	**Amount**
Fruit Punch	1 gal 1 pt
Ginger Ale	2 qt 1 c
Pineapple Juice	1 gal 1 qt
Orange Sherbet	2 qt

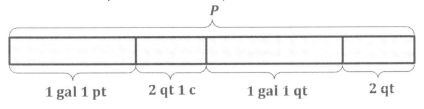

1 gal 1 pt	2 qt 1 c	1 gal 1 qt	2 qt

$$P = 1 \text{ gal } 1 \text{ pt} + 2 \text{ qt } 1 \text{ c} + 1 \text{ gal } 1 \text{ qt} + 2 \text{ qt}$$
$$= 2 \text{ gal } 5 \text{ qt } 1 \text{ pt } 1 \text{ c}$$

1 gal   4 c   2 c

$$= 3 \text{ gal } 7 \text{ c}$$

I could rename this as 3 gallons 1 quart 3 cups, but naming a measurement with 3 units is uncommon. I think to other measurements with 2 units: hours and minutes, weeks and days, feet and inches, pounds and ounces, and dollars and cents.

The recipe makes 3 gallons 7 cups of punch.

b.   How many more cups of liquid would they need to fill a 5-gallon container?

$$3 \text{ gal } 7 \text{ c} \xrightarrow{+9\,c} 4 \text{ gal} \xrightarrow{+16\,c} 5 \text{ gal}$$

They would need 25 more cups of liquid to fill a 5-gallon container.

There are 16 cups in 1 gallon. I count up 9 cups to reach 4 gallons, and then I add 16 cups, or 1 gallon, to reach 5 gallons.

EUREKA MATH

©2015 Great Minds. eureka-math.org
G4-M1-HWH-1.3.0-07.2015

G4-M7-Lesson 7

> 1 ft = 12 in
> 1 yd = 3 ft

1. Determine the following sums and differences. Show your work.

   a. 3 yd 1 ft + 4 ft = __4__ yd __2__ ft

   3 yd 1 ft + 4 ft = 3 yd 5 ft = 4 yd 2 ft
                          ∧
                      1 yd   2 ft

   > I add like units and then rename 5 feet as 1 yard 2 feet. I add 1 yard to 3 yards.

   b. 5 yd − 2 ft = __4__ yd __1__ ft
      ∧
   4 yd   3 ft

   > I rename 5 yards as 4 yards 3 feet in order to subtract 2 feet.

   c. 3 ft 7 in − 8 in = __2__ ft __11__ in
      ∧
   2 ft   19 in

   > I try to subtract like units, but I can't take 8 inches from 7 inches. I rename 3 feet 7 inches as 2 feet 19 inches by taking 1 foot from 3 feet and renaming it as 12 inches and then adding the 7 inches. Then I can subtract 8 inches.

   d. 3 ft 8 in + 4 ft 8 in = __8__ ft __4__ in

   3 ft 8 in + 4 ft 8 in = 7 ft 16 in = 8 ft 4 in
                               ∧
                           1 ft   4 in

2. The height of the tree is 13 feet 8 inches. The height of the bush is 3 feet 10 inches shorter than the height of the tree. What is the height of the bush?

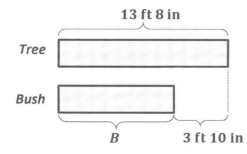

13 ft 8 in − 3 ft 10 in = 9 ft 10 in
                 ∧
         12 ft   20 in

B = 9 ft 10 in

The height of the bush is 9 feet 10 inches.

©2015 Great Minds. eureka-math.org
G4-M1-HWH-1.3.0-07.2015

3. The width of Saisha's rectangular-shaped tree house is 7 feet 6 inches. The perimeter of the tree house is 35 feet.

a. What is the length of Saisha's tree house?

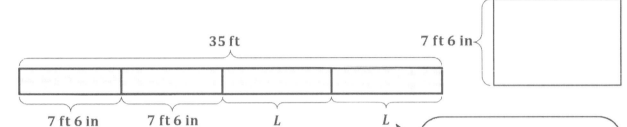

35 ft

7 ft 6 in

7 ft 6 in   7 ft 6 in   L   L

$$7 \text{ ft } 6 \text{ in} + 7 \text{ ft } 6 \text{ in} + L + L = 35 \text{ ft}$$
$$14 \text{ ft } 12 \text{ in} + L + L = 35 \text{ ft}$$
$$15 \text{ ft} + L + L = 35 \text{ ft}$$
$$L + L = 20 \text{ ft}$$
$$L = 10 \text{ ft}$$

The tape diagram helps me to solve this problem. I see that if I subtract the widths from the perimeter that the difference is two times as much as the length.

The length of Saisha's tree house is 10 feet.

I know the perimeter is 35 feet. I subtract the two widths from the perimeter to get the sum of the two lengths.

$$35 \text{ ft} - 15 \text{ ft} = 20 \text{ ft}$$
$$10 \text{ ft} + 10 \text{ ft} = 20 \text{ ft}$$

b. How much longer is the length of Saisha's treehouse than the width?

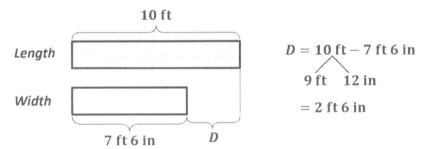

10 ft

Length

Width

7 ft 6 in   D

$$D = 10 \text{ ft} - 7 \text{ ft } 6 \text{ in}$$

9 ft   12 in

$$= 2 \text{ ft } 6 \text{ in}$$

The length of Saisha's treehouse is 2 feet 6 inches longer than the width.

EUREKA MATH

G4-M7-Lesson 8

$$1 \text{ lb} = 16 \text{ oz}$$

1. Determine the following sum and difference. Show your work.

   a.   6 lb 7 oz + 4 lb 9 oz = __11__ lb

   b.   10 lb 4 oz − 4 lb 9 oz = __5__ lb __11__ oz

   6 lb 7 oz + 4 lb 9 oz = 10 lb 16 oz = 11 lb

   $$4 \text{ lb } 9 \text{ oz} \xrightarrow{+7 \text{ oz}} 5 \text{ lb} \xrightarrow{+5 \text{ lb}} 10 \text{ lb} \xrightarrow{+4 \text{ oz}} 10 \text{ lb } 4 \text{ oz}$$

   > Just like adding units of capacity or length, I add like units and rename.

   > I choose to use the arrow way to solve. I count up to reach the next whole pound. I add to find how many I count up in all. That's the same as the difference.

2. On her first birthday, Gwen weighed 23 pounds 12 ounces. On her second birthday, Gwen weighed 30 pounds 8 ounces. How much weight did Gwen gain between her first and second birthday?

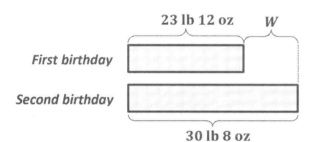

   W = 30 lb 8 oz − 23 lb 12 oz

   29 lb   24 oz

   = 6 lb 12 oz

   > I think of 30 pounds 8 ounces as 29 pounds 16 ounces plus 8 ounces. I subtract like units to get my answer.

   Gwen gained 6 pounds 12 ounces between her first and second birthday.

3. Use the information in the chart about Hayden's school supplies to answer the following question:

   On Monday, Hayden packs her supply case, a notebook, and a textbook into her empty backpack. How much does Hayden's full backpack weigh on Monday?

Textbook 3 lb 8 oz	Supply Case 1 lb	Binder 2 lb 5 oz
Laptop 5 lb 12 oz	Notebook 11 oz	Backpack (empty) 2 lb 14 oz

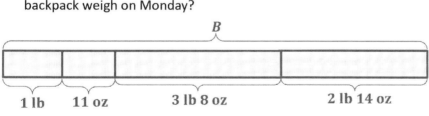

   1 lb   11 oz   3 lb 8 oz   2 lb 14 oz

   B = 1 lb + 11 oz + 3 lb 8 oz + 2 lb 14 oz
     = 6 lb 33 oz

   > I draw a number bond to show 33 ounces as 2 pounds 1 ounce.

        2 lb   1 oz

     = 8 lb 1 oz

   Hayden's full backpack weighed 8 pounds 1 ounce on Monday.

G4-M7-Lesson 9

1 day = 24 hr
1 hr = 60 min
1 min = 60 sec

1. Determine the following sum and difference. Show your work.

   a. 6 hr 26 min + 4 hr 41 min = __11__ hr _7_ min

   6 hr 26 min + 4 hr 41 min = 10 hr 67 min = 11 hr 7 min

   1 hr   7 min

   > I add like units just as with fractions or other measurement units.

   b. 36 min 42 sec − 24 min 56 sec = __11__ min __46__ sec

   36 min 42 sec − 24 min 56 sec = 36 min 46 sec − 25 min = 11 min 46 sec
   +4 sec   +4 sec

   > I use compensation as a strategy to solve. I add 4 seconds to each time. The difference remains the same. Subtracting just one unit, minutes, is easier than subtracting mixed units.

2. Ciera finished the race in 3 minutes 31 seconds. She beat Sarah's time by 47 seconds. What was Sarah's time?

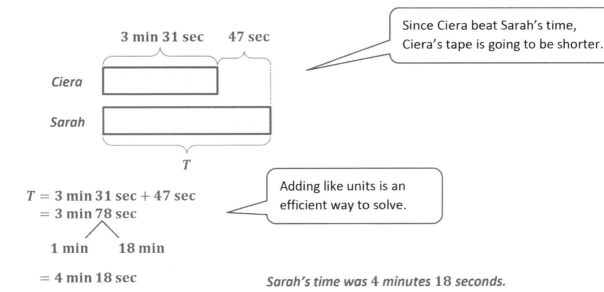

> Since Ciera beat Sarah's time, Ciera's tape is going to be shorter.

3 min 31 sec   47 sec

Ciera

Sarah

T

$T = 3\ min\ 31\ sec + 47\ sec$
$= 3\ min\ 78\ sec$

1 min   18 min

$= 4\ min\ 18\ sec$

> Adding like units is an efficient way to solve.

Sarah's time was 4 minutes 18 seconds.

©2015 Great Minds. eureka-math.org
G4-M1-HWH-1.3.0-07.2015

G4-M7-Lesson 10

1. On Saturday, Andrew used 1 pint 1 cup of paint from a full gallon container to paint the porch steps. On Sunday, he used twice as much paint from the container as he did on Saturday. How much paint was left in the container after Sunday?

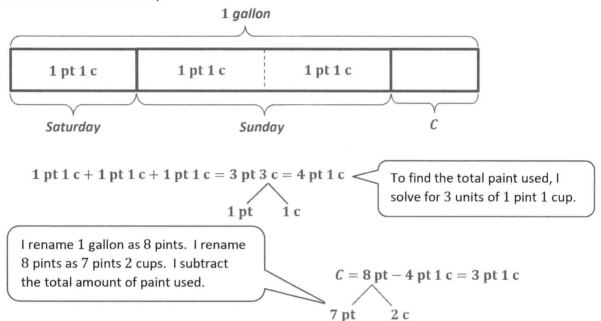

There were 3 pints 1 cup of paint left in the container after Sunday.

2. Shyan is 4 feet 7 inches tall. Her brother is 1 foot 5 inches taller than she is, and her sister is half as tall as her brother. How tall is Shyan's sister?

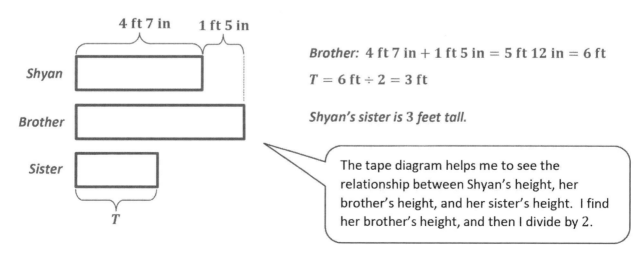

Brother: $4 \text{ ft } 7 \text{ in} + 1 \text{ ft } 5 \text{ in} = 5 \text{ ft } 12 \text{ in} = 6 \text{ ft}$

$T = 6 \text{ ft} \div 2 = 3 \text{ ft}$

Shyan's sister is 3 feet tall.

The tape diagram helps me to see the relationship between Shyan's height, her brother's height, and her sister's height. I find her brother's height, and then I divide by 2.

G4-M7-Lesson 11

1. A rectangular sidewalk is 2 feet 9 inches wide. Its length is three times the width plus 5 more inches. How long is the sidewalk?

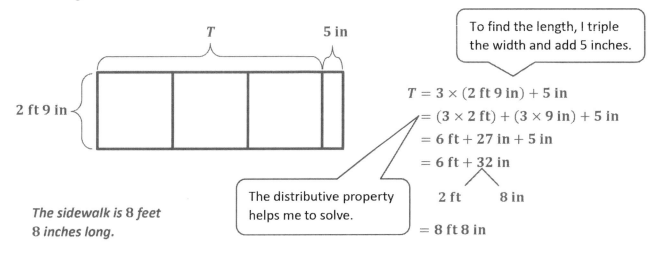

To find the length, I triple the width and add 5 inches.

$T = 3 \times (2 \text{ ft } 9 \text{ in}) + 5 \text{ in}$
$= (3 \times 2 \text{ ft}) + (3 \times 9 \text{ in}) + 5 \text{ in}$
$= 6 \text{ ft} + 27 \text{ in} + 5 \text{ in}$
$= 6 \text{ ft} + 32 \text{ in}$

2 ft   8 in

The distributive property helps me to solve.

$= 8 \text{ ft } 8 \text{ in}$

The sidewalk is 8 feet 8 inches long.

2. Mr. Lalonde plans to make his world-famous cookies. He has 2 pounds 3 ounces of brown sugar. This is $\frac{1}{3}$ of the total amount of brown sugar needed. If he uses 7 ounces of brown sugar for each batch of cookies, how many batches of cookies can he make?

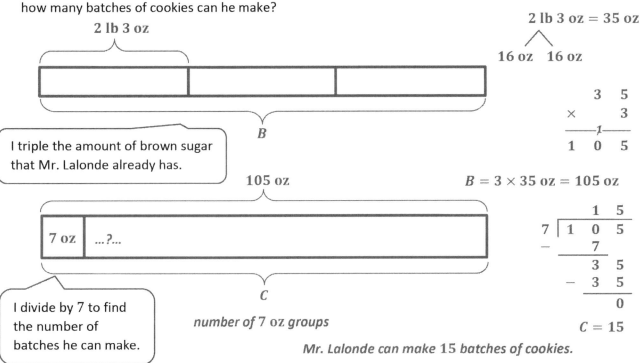

2 lb 3 oz = 35 oz

16 oz   16 oz

```
      3   5
  ×       3
 ---1-----
  1   0   5
```

I triple the amount of brown sugar that Mr. Lalonde already has.

$B = 3 \times 35 \text{ oz} = 105 \text{ oz}$

```
          1   5
     7 | 1   0   5
     -     7
         ----
           3   5
     -     3   5
         ----
               0
```

I divide by 7 to find the number of batches he can make.

number of 7 oz groups

$C = 15$

Mr. Lalonde can make 15 batches of cookies.

EUREKA
MATH

©2015 Great Minds. eureka-math.org
G4-M1-HWH-1.3.0-07.2015

3. Rocket exercised for 2 hours 27 minutes each day for 5 days. He spent an equal amount of time on lower body, upper body, and cardio. How long did he spend on cardio during the five-day period?

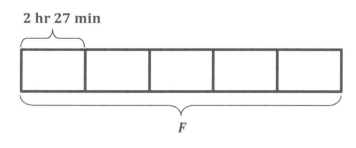

$F = 5 \times 2 \text{ hr } 27 \text{ min}$

$= (5 \times 2 \text{ hr}) + (5 \times 27 \text{ min})$

$= 10 \text{ hr } 135 \text{ min}$

2 hr   15 min

$= 12 \text{ hr } 15 \text{ min}$

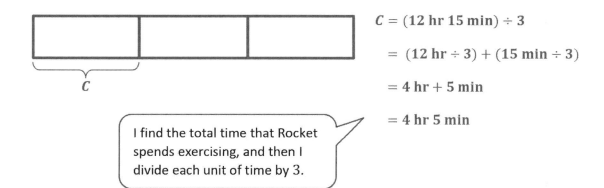

$C = (12 \text{ hr } 15 \text{ min}) \div 3$

$= (12 \text{ hr} \div 3) + (15 \text{ min} \div 3)$

$= 4 \text{ hr} + 5 \text{ min}$

$= 4 \text{ hr } 5 \text{ min}$

I find the total time that Rocket spends exercising, and then I divide each unit of time by 3.

Rocket spent 4 hours 5 minutes on cardio during the five-day period.

©2015 Great Minds. eureka-math.org
G4-M1-HWH-1.3.0-07.2015

G4-M7-Lesson 12

1. Draw a tape diagram to show $1\frac{2}{3}$ yards = 5 feet.

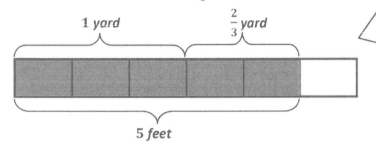

I know that 1 yard = 3 feet, so I can decompose each yard in my tape diagram into 3 feet. I can shade in $1\frac{2}{3}$ yards, and since each unit is $\frac{1}{3}$ yard, or 1 foot, I can see that $1\frac{2}{3}$ yards is equal to 5 feet.

2. Solve the problems using whatever tool works best for you.

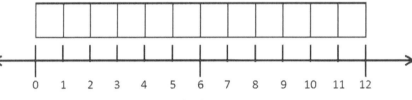

1 foot

inches

a. $\frac{6}{12}$ foot = __6__ inches

b. $\frac{9}{12}$ foot = $\frac{3}{4}$ foot = __9__ inches

c. $\frac{8}{12}$ foot = $\frac{4}{6}$ foot = __8__ inches

For part (a), I know that $\frac{6}{12}$ foot $= \frac{1}{2}$ foot, and I know that half a foot is 6 inches. For parts (b) and (c), I can make equivalent fractions and then find the number of inches. $\frac{3 \times 3}{4 \times 3} = \frac{9}{12}$. $\frac{9}{12}$ foot is the same as 9 inches.

Lesson 12:   Use measurement tools to convert mixed number measurements to
                            smaller units.

EUREKA MATH

3. Solve.

a. $5\frac{1}{3}$ yd = ___16___ ft

15 ⁄ 1
feet   foot

1 yard = 3 feet, so 5 yards = 5×3 feet = 15 feet. And $\frac{1}{3}$ yard = 1 foot. 15 feet + 1 foot = 16 feet.

b. $4\frac{3}{4}$ gal = ___19___ qt

16   3
quarts quarts

1 gallon = 4 quarts, so 4 gallons = 4×4 quarts = 16 quarts. And $\frac{1}{4}$ gallon = 1 quart, so $\frac{3}{4}$ gallon = 3 quarts. 16 quarts + 3 quarts = 19 quarts.

c. $3\frac{1}{3}$ ft = ___40___ in

36   4
inches inches

1 foot = 12 inches, so 3 feet = 3×12 inches = 36 inches. And $\frac{1}{12}$ foot = 1 inch, so $\frac{1}{3} = \frac{1 \times 4}{3 \times 4} = \frac{4}{12}$. $\frac{4}{12}$ foot equals 4 inches. 36 inches + 4 inches = 40 inches.

G4-M7-Lesson 13

1. Solve.

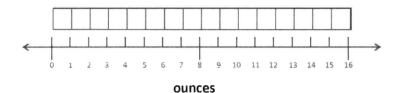

ounces

a. $\frac{2}{16}$ pound = ___2___ ounces

b. $\frac{8}{16}$ pound = $\frac{2}{4}$ pound = ___8___ ounces

c. $\frac{6}{16}$ pound = $\frac{3}{8}$ pound = ___6___ ounces

> For part (a), I know that $\frac{1}{16}$ pound = 1 ounce, so $\frac{2}{16}$ pound = 2 ounces. For part
> (b), I know that $\frac{2}{4}$ pound = $\frac{1}{2}$ pound, which is equal to $\frac{8}{16}$ pound or 8 ounces. For
> part (c), I can make equivalent fractions. $\frac{3 \times 2}{8 \times 2} = \frac{6}{16}$. And $\frac{6}{16}$ pound = 6 ounces.

2. Draw a tape diagram to show $1\frac{1}{8}$ pounds = 18 ounces.

1 pound $\frac{1}{8}$ *pound*

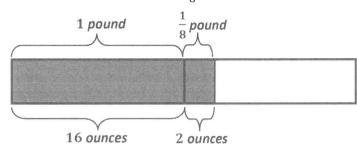

16 ounces   *2 ounces*

16 ounces + 2 ounces = 18 ounces

> I can draw a tape diagram that shows $1\frac{1}{8}$ pounds. Then I can convert the pounds
> to ounces. 1 pound = 16 ounces. I can use an equivalent fraction to figure out
> how many ounces are in $\frac{1}{8}$ pound. $\frac{1 \times 2}{8 \times 2} = \frac{2}{16}$, so $\frac{1}{8}$ pound = 2 ounces.

EUREKA MATH

3. Solve.

1 hour

0 1 2 3 4 5 6 7 8 9 10 11 12 13 14 15 16 17 18 19 20 21 22 23 24 25 26 27 28 29 30 31 32 33 34 35 36 37 38 39 40 41 42 43 44 45 46 47 48 49 50 51 52 53 54 55 56 57 58 59 60

minutes

a. $\frac{45}{60}$ hour $= \frac{3}{4}$ hour $=$ ___**45**___ minutes

b. $\frac{40}{60}$ hour $= \frac{2}{3}$ hour $=$ ___**40**___ minutes

> For part (a), I know that $\frac{1}{4}$ hour = 15 minutes, so $\frac{3}{4}$ hour = 45 minutes = $\frac{45}{60}$ hour.
> For part (b), I know that $\frac{1}{3}$ hour = 20 minutes, so $\frac{2}{3}$ hour = 40 minutes = $\frac{40}{60}$ hour.

4. Solve.

a. $3\frac{5}{8}$ pounds = ___**58**___ ounces	b. $4\frac{1}{4}$ lb = ___**68**___ oz	c. $2\frac{3}{4}$ hours = ___**165**___ minutes
48 10 oz oz	64 4 oz oz	120 45 min min

> 1 pound = 16 ounces, so 3 pounds = 3 × 16 ounces = 48 ounces. And $\frac{1}{8}$ pound = 2 ounces, so $\frac{5}{8}$ pound = 10 ounces. 48 ounces + 10 ounces = 58 ounces.

> 4 pounds = 4 × 16 ounces = 64 ounces. And $\frac{1}{4}$ pound = 4 ounces. 64 ounces + 4 ounces = 68 ounces.

> 1 hour = 60 minutes, so 2 hours = 2 × 60 minutes = 120 minutes. And $\frac{1}{4}$ hour = 15 minutes, so $\frac{3}{4}$ hour = 45 minutes. 120 minutes + 45 minutes = 165 minutes.

EUREKA MATH™

©2015 Great Minds. eureka-math.org
G4-M1-HWH-1.3.0-07.2015

G4-M7-Lesson 14

Use RDW to solve the following problems.

1. Doug practiced piano for 1 hour and 50 minutes on Monday. On Tuesday, he practiced piano for 25 minutes less than Monday. How many minutes did Doug practice piano on Monday and Tuesday?

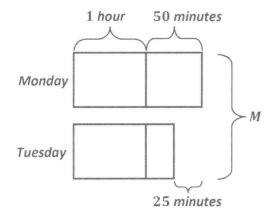

I can draw a tape diagram to represent the amount of time that Doug practiced piano each day. The tape for Monday is longer than Tuesday's because he practiced for 25 minutes less on Tuesday.

1 hour 50 minutes − 25 minutes = 1 hour 25 minutes

I subtract 25 minutes from Monday's time to figure out how long Doug practiced on Tuesday.

1 hour 50 minutes + 1 hour 25 minutes = 2 hours 75 minutes

2 hours 75 minutes = 120 minutes + 75 minutes = 195 minutes

M = 195 minutes

I add the times for Monday and Tuesday to find the total time. Then I convert the hours to minutes. 1 hour = 60 minutes, so 2 hours = 120 minutes.

Doug practiced piano for 195 minutes on Monday and Tuesday.

Lesson 14:   Solve multi-step word problems involving converting mixed number
                     measurements to a single unit.

EUREKA
MATH

2. Ella can make 15 bracelets from a 105-inch piece of cord.

   a. How many inches of cord would be needed to make 60 bracelets?

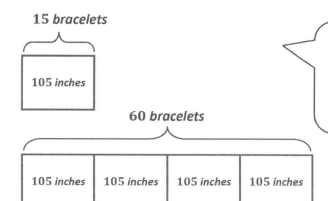

15 bracelets

105 inches

60 bracelets

105 inches | 105 inches | 105 inches | 105 inches

> I can draw 1 unit of 105 inches to represent the length of cord needed to make 15 bracelets. I can draw 4 units of 105 inches to represent the length of cord needed to make 60 bracelets because $4 \times 15 = 60$.

4×105 inches $= 420$ inches

$$\begin{array}{r} 1\ 0\ 5 \\ \times\ \ \ \ 4 \\ \hline 4\ 2\ 0 \end{array}$$

> To find the total number of inches of cord that Ella needs to make 60 bracelets, I can multiply 4×105 inches.

Ella needs 420 inches of cord to make 60 bracelets.

   b. Extension: The cord Ella uses to make bracelets is also sold in $8\frac{1}{3}$-foot packages. How many packages would be needed to make 60 bracelets?

$8\frac{1}{3}$ feet $= 100$ inches

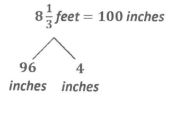

96　　4
inches　inches

> I can covert $8\frac{1}{3}$ feet to inches. 8×12 inches $= 96$ inches and $\frac{1}{3}$ foot $= 4$ inches. 96 inches $+$ 4 inches $= 100$ inches. Ella would need to buy 5 packages because 4 packages would only be 400 inches of cord and she needs 420 inches of cord.

5×100 inches $= 500$ inches

Ella would need 5 packages to make 60 bracelets.

EUREKA MATH | **Lesson 14:** Solve multi-step word problems involving converting mixed number measurements to a single unit. | 25

©2015 Great Minds. eureka-math.org
G4-M1-HWH-1.3.0-07.2015

G4-M7-Lesson 15

1. Find the area of the figure that is shaded.

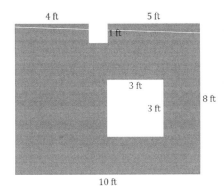

> I find the area of the white portion inside the shaded figure and the area of the cutout.

$3 \text{ ft} \times 3 \text{ ft} = 9 \text{ square ft}$

$1 \text{ ft} \times 1 \text{ ft} = 1 \text{ square ft}$

$9 \text{ square ft} + 1 \text{ square ft} = 10 \text{ square ft}$

$10 \text{ ft} \times 8 \text{ ft} = 80 \text{ square ft}$

> I think of the shaded area as a rectangle without the cutouts and find its area.

$80 \text{ square ft} - 10 \text{ square ft} = 70 \text{ square ft}$

> I subtract the area of the cutouts from the area of the larger rectangle to find the area of the figure that is shaded.

The area of the shaded figure is 70 square feet.

2. A wall is 10 feet tall and 12 feet wide. A window with a width of 2 feet and a height of 4 feet is in the center of the wall. Find the area of the wall that can be painted.

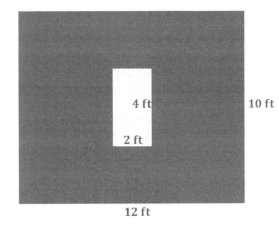

$12 \text{ ft} \times 10 \text{ ft} = 120 \text{ square ft}$

$2 \text{ ft} \times 4 \text{ ft} = 8 \text{ square ft}$

$120 \text{ square ft} - 8 \text{ square ft} = 112 \text{ square ft}$

The area of the wall that can be painted is 112 square feet.

©2015 Great Minds. eureka-math.org
G4-M1-HWH-1.3.0-07.2015

G4-M7-Lesson 16

1. Use a ruler and protractor to create and shade a figure according to the directions:

    Draw a rectangle that is 15 centimeters long and 5 centimeters wide. Inside the rectangle, draw a smaller rectangle that is 10 centimeters long and 4 centimeters wide. Inside the smaller rectangle, draw a square that has side lengths of 2 centimeters. Shade the larger rectangle and the square.

    Find the area of the shaded space.

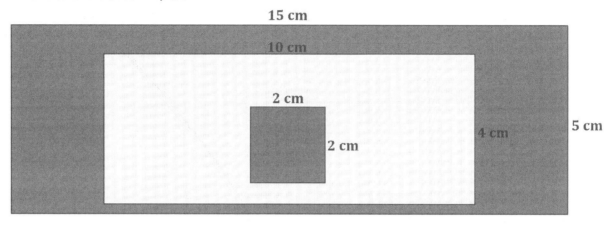

Large rectangle: $15\text{ cm} \times 10\text{ cm} = 150$ *square cm*

Small rectangle: $10\text{ cm} \times 4\text{ cm} = 40$ *square cm*

$150\text{ square cm} - 40\text{ square cm} = 110$ *square cm*

Square: $2\text{ cm} \times 2\text{ cm} = 4$ *square cm*

$110\text{ square cm} + 4\text{ square cm} = 114$ *square cm*

The area of the shaded space is 114 *square centimeters.*

> To find the area of the shaded space, I subtract the area of the smaller, unshaded rectangle from the area of the larger, shaded rectangle, and add back the area of the square.

2. Zachary hangs a television that is 4 feet long and 2 feet wide on a wall that is 10 feet long and 8 feet tall. How much area of the wall is not covered up by the television?

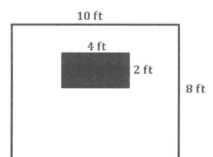

Wall: $8\text{ ft} \times 10\text{ ft} = 80$ *square ft*

TV: $2\text{ ft} \times 4\text{ ft} = 8$ *square ft*

$80\text{ square ft} - 8\text{ square ft} = 72$ *square ft*

72 *square feet of the wall is not covered by the television.*

G4-M7-Lesson 17

1. Plot and label each point on the number line below, and complete the chart.

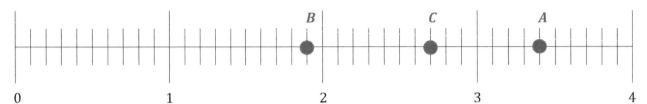

Point	Unit Form	Decimal Form	Mixed Number (ones and fraction form)	How much more to get to the next whole number?
A	3 ones 4 tenths	3.4	$3\frac{4}{10}$	0.6
B	**1 one 9 tenths**	1.9	$1\frac{9}{10}$	0.1
C	**2 ones 7 tenths**	2.7	$2\frac{7}{10}$	$\frac{3}{10}$ or 0.3

> To solve for point C, I named two and seven tenths, but I could have named any decimal that is 3 tenths from a whole number between zero and four: 0.7, 1.7, or 3.7.

2. Complete the chart.

Decimal	Mixed Number	Tenths	Hundredths
5.8	$5\frac{8}{10}$	58 *tenths or* $\frac{58}{10}$	580 *hundredths or* $\frac{580}{100}$
9.2	$9\frac{2}{10}$	92 *tenths or* $\frac{92}{10}$	920 *hundredths or* $\frac{920}{100}$

> I convert 9.2 to $9\frac{20}{100}$ to help me write the number as hundredths.

Lesson 17:   Practice and solidify Grade 4 fluency.

EUREKA MATH